CLASSIFICATION OF THE ANIMAL KINGDOM

an illustrated guide

HODDER AND STOUGHTON LTD
THE READER'S DIGEST ASSOCIATION LTD

INTRODUCTION

by Richard Freeman M.B.E., M.A.
Reader in Zoology, University College, London.

Animal types in everyday terms

Invertebrates

Most of the living species of animals are invertebrates—animals without backbones. They entirely fill 25 of the 26 phyla into which the animal kingdom is divided

Fish

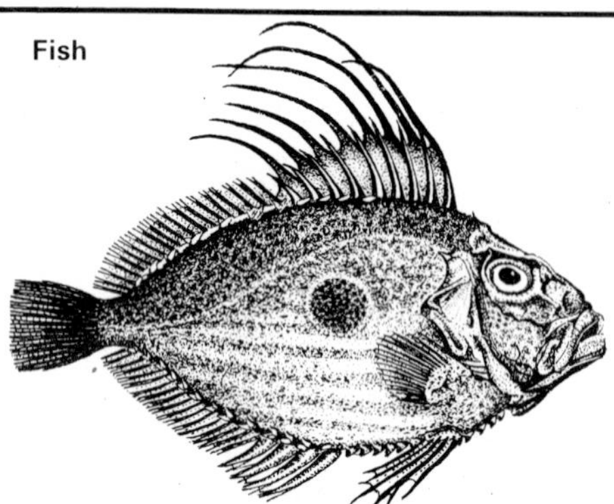

Together with amphibians, reptiles, birds and mammals, fish belong in the sub-phylum Vertebrata—animals with backbones. There are three classes of fish, each as distinct from the others as mammals are from birds, reptiles and amphibians

Amphibians

Amphibians, the most primitive class of land-living vertebrates, usually begin their lives in water and most of the adults return to it to breed. There are three orders of amphibians—newts and salamanders; frogs and toads; and caecilians

Reptiles

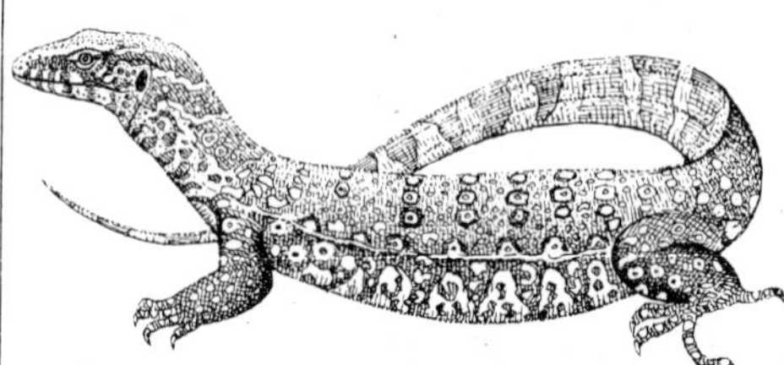

There are four orders in the reptile class—turtles and tortoises; lizards and snakes; crocodiles; and the tuatara, a lizard-like animal which is the sole survivor of its group. Other species in the tuatara order have been extinct for 100 million years

Birds

There are 27 orders of birds, grouped in the class Aves. They differ from reptiles, from which they have evolved, by having feathers and wings and being warm-blooded

Mammals

There are three types of mammals—monotremes, which lay eggs; marsupials, which give birth to poorly developed young and usually raise them in a pouch; and placentals, whose young are more advanced at birth

There is one imperative reason for naming different kinds of animals, and one for classifying them. The reason for naming them is for communication. Nobody wants to observe animals or experiment with them unless he can tell other people of like interests what he has discovered, and to do this each kind, and each group of kinds, must have names which are concise, universally understood, and as accurate as possible. The reason for classifying them, that is to say placing them in hierarchies of higher groups, each containing more and more kinds, is so that we can study the relationships of each kind, and of each group, with others.

Let us consider names first. It might appear that vernacular names are accurate and concise, and the use of dictionaries would provide universal equivalents, but there are several reasons why this is not so. Lexicographers are not systematic biologists and do not understand the niceties of naming, nor indeed have they the space to consider them. Even within the vocabulary of a single language there are difficulties. The largest kind of deer in the world is known as the elk in England, but English speakers in the New World call it the moose and use the name elk, as well as the name wapiti, for what is known in England as the red deer. The robin in North America is a bird as large as a thrush whilst the bird of that name in England is quite different and much smaller. In Australia the name is used for several flycatchers, and in Jamaica for the tiny green todies. The only character that all have in common is the presence of some red feathering on throat and breast.

But much more important than this is that there are far more kinds of animals than there are vernacular names. Something well over a million kinds have been described and the very great majority of them have no vernacular names in any language. In the birds, which are better known than any other group, probably every kind, except the few yet to be discovered, has a name in English and other widely used European languages which would be understood by most ornithologists, but this is not true of any other group, not even of the mammals.

So far we have written of kinds of animals; by kind we have meant species and this word must be defined before we can see how animals are named. In matters of names alone, an almost entirely satisfactory definition of a species is the fundamentalist one. A species is the original pair of animals created by God, and all their subsequent offspring. We recognize them today as kinds which will mate only amongst themselves and produce fertile offspring in the wild. No biologist believes such a definition but it serves well for naming.

The method of naming that we use is a very old one, stemming originally from Greek philosophers who used it to name any group of objects, but it has been modified to suit biological needs. The language used is Latin, Latin that would often be incomprehensible to Romans, but nevertheless using Latin constructions and Latin genders. In the early days, up to the middle of the eighteenth century, the name of a species consisted of a generic name, a single word written with a capital initial letter, representing the name of a number of groups of objects which were considered sufficiently alike to belong to the same genus, followed by a specific epithet, usually of a few words, sometimes but not often of one only, which were considered sufficient to distinguish each species in a genus from any other one. For example, Francis Willughby, in 1676, in his work on all the species of birds then known, *Ornithologiae libri tres*, in his treatment of thrushes calls the mistle thrush *Turdus viscivorus major*, the large mistletoe-eating thrush; the common thrush is *Turdus simpliciter dictus sive viscivorus minor*, that is the thrush which is simply known as the thrush or the small mistletoe thrush. Only the fieldfare, *Turdus pilaris*, has a name of two words only.

The modifications of this system which we use at the present time were first developed, and consistently used, by Carolus Linnaeus (1707–1778). Linnaeus was a Swede, a physician, and a botanist more than a zoologist. He was Professor of Medicine at the University of Uppsala from 1741 until his death, a time when a wealth of new species were being discovered, especially by travellers in exotic lands. Though a good student of nature, he was above all a classifier, and he needed a system of classification, and a uniform system of nomenclature to go with it, by which he could handle the mass of material which came to him, and make it and its relationships understandable to other people. Much of his system of classification has not stood the test of time, but his nomenclature has, and is with us, little altered, today. After 1754, when he was ennobled, he was sometimes known as Carl von Linné, and in England as Sir Charles Linneus. His writings are numerous, but the most important to zoologists is the *Systema naturae* in which he describes the species of the three kingdoms of nature: animal, vegetable and mineral. The first edition was a slim folio in 1735, but it is in the 10th edition of 1758 that he first uses his system of nomenclature uniformly for animals and plants, and it is this edition which forms the starting point for all generic and specific names of animals, previous names being ignored.

In the Linnaean system, the generic name continues to be a single Latin substantive. In the name of a species, the genus is followed by a single Latin word, always written with a small initial letter. This is the specific name, and the two words together are known as the scientific name. The specific name is often an adjective, in which case it must agree in gender with the generic name, but it can also be a substantive in apposition or a proper noun in the genitive. Taking examples again from the thrushes, in the American robin, *Turdus migratorius*, the specific name is an adjective agreeing with *Turdus* which is masculine; in the blackbird, *Turdus merula*, it is a substantive in apposition; in the Siberian thrush, *Turdus sibiricus*, it is a place name; in the dusky thrush, *Turdus naumanni*, it is a male personal name; it would have been *naumannae* had Naumann been a woman. Generic and scientific names are always printed in italics, and are therefore always underlined in typescript or manuscript.

These names are sufficient in themselves to identify any species, but it is often useful to give the name of the person who originally described the species, and sometimes the date of its first use. In the case of Linnaeus we write just L., but in all other cases the surname is written out in full; we write *Turdus migratorius* L., but *Turdus sibiricus* Pallas. If a species was originally described in one genus and later transferred to, or split off into, another, then the author's name is placed in parentheses (); thus the rock thrush was described in *Turdus* by Linnaeus, but is now in the genus *Monticola* and its name is written *Monticola saxatilis* (L).

This system is simple, and, purely from a point of view of names, it works well on the whole, but there are certain difficulties. The most important of these are what happens when the same species is given a different specific or scientific name by two different authorities, or even by the same authority, and conversely what happens when two different species are given the same name? There are many more such problems and the answers to them are given in an international code of rules. This was last published in 1961, and there is an international panel of commissioners who give rulings in difficult cases. In the first question asked above the two names are called **synonyms**, and the answer to it is that the name given first is the correct one, subject to certain provisos. In the second question the two names are **homonyms**, and the answer is that the species that was named first keeps that name, again subject to certain provisos. The whole system is intended to produce stability of names and on the whole it does so, but anyone who has read the literature of even the best known groups of animals will know how frequently names have to be changed for purely nomenclatorial reasons.

The rules are concerned not only with generic and specific names but also with higher categories up as far as families (but no further), with one lower category, the subspecies, and between the genus and the species, the subgenus. The usual categories above the genus are subtribes, tribes, subfamilies, families and superfamilies. The rules

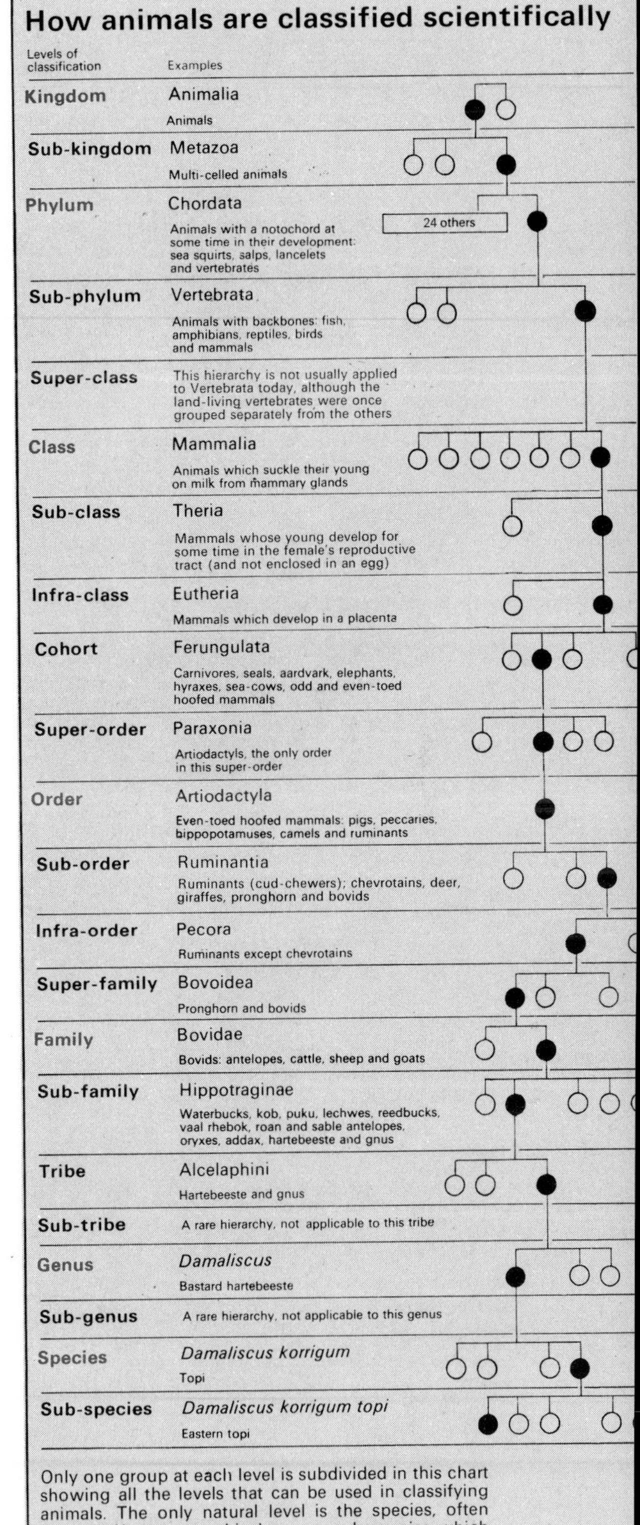

Only one group at each level is subdivided in this chart showing all the levels that can be used in classifying animals. The only natural level is the species, often separated into geographical races, or sub-species, which generally differ in appearance

say that families are named by placing the suffix -idae after the root of the type genus of the family, and subfamilies -inae. By custom subtribes take -ina, tribes -ini, and superfamilies -oidea. A 'type' is little more than a nomenclatorial device; the describer of any new species must designate a single specimen as the type or holotype; the describer of any new genus must designate one of the contained species; and the describer of any higher category, a contained genus. In any given higher classification not all the divisions are necessarily used, and in some further divisions may be inserted. In general, the greater the number of species in any group the further it is likely to be divided up.

The subgenus is a useful device for breaking up genera which have a large number of contained species into component groups whose members seem to be more like each other than they are like other members of the genus. By using the subgenus, well established and widely known generic names can be preserved. For example, Linnaeus put the lion, *Felis leo*, in the same genus as the domestic cat. Some authorities prefer to break up the genus into smaller units and place the lion with other big cats in the genus *Panthera*; others prefer to retain the genus *Felis* and to treat *Panthera* as a subgenus. In which case the scientific name of the lion would be *Felis (Panthera) leo*.

The subspecies is difficult to define, but in general if different populations within a species can be shown to differ consistently from other populations then they can be treated as subspecies and given subspecific names. The differences are usually morphological, size, shape and often colour, but may be purely physiological or even behavioural. Many subspecies represent isolated populations on islands or mountains, but others may be contiguous mainland populations, when they may pass into the next subspecies either gradually or abruptly.

The peregrine falcon, or duck hawk as it is called in North America, *Falco peregrinus*, is almost world wide in distribution and has some 15 described subspecies. That of the western Palaearctic is the form which was originally described as the species and is known as the nominate subspecies, or, less sensibly, as the typical subspecies although it is no more typical than any other. Its name in subspecific form is written *Falco peregrinus peregrinus*, or for short *Falco p. peregrinus*. The duck hawk of Greenland and North America is different in colouration and is called *Falco peregrinus anatum*. The wren, or winter wren of North America, *Troglodytes troglodytes*, has a Holarctic distribution and a number of subspecies, many of them on islands. Around the British coasts there are *T. t. fridariensis* on Fair Isle, *T. t. hebridensis* in the Outer Hebrides, *T. t. hirtensis* on St. Kilda, and *T. t. zetlandicus* in the Shetland Islands. Some authorities, but not all, believe that the population on mainland Britain can be distinguished from that of continental Europe as *T. t. indigenus*.

Above the superfamily and below the subspecies, although there are no formal rules of nomenclature either for what categories to use or how to name them, certain customs have grown up which are normally followed. In the higher categories, above genus, Linnaeus used only order, class and kingdom, but the family was introduced in his lifetime. Today, we still use these four categories with phylum, introduced by Ernst Haeckel in the late nineteenth century, added between class and kingdom. Further groups can be made by adding the prefixes super-, sub- and infra- to any of these major divisions. For example we can have Superclass, Class, Subclass, Infraclass, Superorder, Order and so on, although such complex hierarchies are only used in the larger groups. The fully expanded classification of one of the topi antelopes of central Africa is shown on page 2. The names used are latinized, but usually there are no formal endings, as there are with family to subtribe groups, so that it is not possible to tell at a glance what level each name indicates. There are a few exceptions to this; for example, in one of the most used classifications of birds all the ordinal names are derived from the root of the type genus of some 'typical' contained family with the addition of the suffix -formes. Thus Piciformes are woodpeckers, from the genus *Picus*; Anseriformes are geese and ducks, from the genus *Anser*. Similarly, almost all the orders of winged insects have the suffix -ptera, although here the root does not come from a generic name but from some attribute; Coleoptera are beetles, sheath wings; Lepidoptera are butterflies and moths, scale wings.

In the great majority of cases these names are uniformly accepted throughout the world, although there are cases where some people use one name and some another. The phylum which contains the moss animals can be called Polyzoa, Bryozoa or Ectoprocta. Fleas are Siphonaptera to English-speaking peoples but Aphaniptera in continental Europe. All higher category names from Subtribe to Kingdom take initial capital letters and are printed in roman, not italic.

Below the subspecies there is less uniformity of custom. In the great collecting days of the nineteenth century it was customary to give latin names to forms, varieties and aberrations such as specimens or series which differed from what was considered normal, in a rather vague way. Form was usually used where a whole local population differed from the rest, and these have now mostly become subspecies. Variety was usually used for those which were found regularly but more or less infrequently in otherwise normal populations, and aberration for the very infrequent and freakish. This was at a time when little or nothing was known of the inheritance of variation or of polymorphism in general. Some of these Latin names survive, particularly amongst collectors, and may serve as a useful shorthand for those who know the genetic background, but they often lend a spurious respectability to ignorance. In general, such variation is now described in the vernacular, and indeed there has been a tendency in recent years to use the formal subspecies less, because it gives rise to too rigid a picture of what the situation actually is in the wild.

We must now consider briefly the methods by which we examine animals and decide what their relationships are, and thence where to put them in the scheme. The method that we use is not a new one but derives from that used by the early civilizations of the Mediterranean to sort any set of phenomena. We examine the material, perhaps a single specimen if that is all that we have got, but preferably a sample of a population, and list its characters, taking as many characters as possible. The characters are mostly morphological, but whenever possible physiological, behavioural and genetic ones should also be considered. We then compare it with other sets of material, or descriptions of other known sets, and see whether it agrees exactly with any of them. If it does agree exactly then it belongs to that set; if the agreement is close to some set but not exact then we can place our new set close to the next nearest.

If the set is a sample from a wild population of animals and we find that it does agree exactly with some other set then we know that it belongs to a species or a subspecies which has already been described, and we can not only find out what is already known about it but also put it in its place in the whole hierarchy. If it is not known, then we must decide how near it is to some set which is known. The experience of the describer will tell him whether it can be fitted into a known genus or whether a new genus or other higher categories are needed. Today, the animal kingdom is well known and in most cases our set will not even need a new genus, but will fit as a species or subspecies within the already known system. But even as recently as 1938 it was necessary to erect a new phylum, the Pogonophora, for certain living animals. One species had been described shortly after the turn of the century, but so little was known about it that it was not possible to fit it into the system. More species have been discovered since then, which were found to have characters so unlike those of any other animals that the only way of placing them was to erect a new phylum. A few other living animals have been discovered recently which call for new classes and orders, but such events are exceptional.

Higher classifications are not static things. In Linnaeus' day so little was known about the structure of invertebrate animals that he felt it best to put all of them, except the arthropods, into one class, the Vermes, with seven orders. Today these correspond to about 20 phyla with numerous classes and orders. This increase is in part due to increase in knowledge which showed that groups previously thought to be related either are not related, or are less closely related; but it is also due to the increase in the number of described species so as to prevent large groups becoming too unwieldy. Higher classifications are also not static for another reason. This is that different experts differ in their views as to how the known facts of relationship are best expressed in the hierarchies. For example, the phylum Aschelminthes was erected to bring together six groups which had previously been treated as six separate phyla or in various other combinations. Aschelminthes was used in an important textbook and has been widely taught as a phylum ever since. Other experts would however assert that either there is not enough evidence for combining the six or that the evidence is doubtfully correct. They would revert to the six phyla or use other combinations.

In comparing sets of characters, should more weight be put on the importance given to any one character than to any other? In early classifications, it was a rule that at any given level all the different groups should be differentiated on the same character. Thus Linnaeus divided the mammals into orders on their dentition, which gave some peculiar results. For example rhinoceroses went with mice, and manatees with sloths. Provided that sufficient characters are taken it is best that they should be given equal weight.

At the bottom of a hierarchy the individuals of closely related sets will have a great many characters in common, and in some cases it is found that discrete sets exist which are morphologically indistinguishable. Such sets of species are known as siblings. They are recognized on physiological or behavioural characters including the fact that they will not cross with the production of fertile offspring in the wild. Once they have been recognized, careful re-examination may reveal minute morphological differences which had previously been overlooked. At the top end of the hierarchy the number of characters common to all members is small. Thus in the phylum Chordata almost the only common characters are the presence of a notochord, dorsal nerve cord, endostyle and gills at some stage of the life history. The only common character to all members of the animal kingdom, if such a division is retained, is that at some stage they feed in a holozoic manner, that is to say they eat organic substances which have originally been made from inorganic by plants.

Finally, it must be remembered that the animals made themselves, but the various groups were made by man. We made them and we can unmake them if they fail to indicate the facts or to convey to others the information which we want them to convey. But why do we need to classify at all? The original reason, and the continuing reason in vulgar speech is, as with names, one of communication. We need to teach our young to recognize those groups of natural objects which are edible, or dangerous, or useful in curing disease, and so on. Consequently, vernacular classifications do not, as a rule, extend very far. In English we have words for beasts (i.e. mammals), birds and fishes but no vernacular for vertebrates in general. We have words for a few groups of insects such as beetles, butterflies and moths, but insect is itself a modern word which is still, more often than not, misused by those with no biological training.

A second but later reason for classifying is the scientific inquisitiveness, divorced from any importance to man's life, which emerged in the seventeenth century under the influence of Francis Bacon. The existence of man, and of nature in general, argued the existence of a creator, and from the late seventeenth century to late in the nineteenth the study of patterns of classification was presumed to give information about the attributes of a christian God. Works such as John Ray's *Wisdom of God* (1691) and William Paley's *Natural theology* (1802) stressed the importance of classification in the study of nature and were widely read.

The real reason why classifications show the patterns of relationship that they do did not become apparent until the acceptance of the general theory of evolution. The idea that animals had evolved, rather than being created as they are, had been put forward many times from the Greeks onwards, but it did not receive any general acceptance until after the publication of Charles Darwin's *On the origin of species* in 1859. Even then the acceptance was gradual. Those who accepted the theory saw at once, as did Darwin, that animals showed the relationships that they did because these were relationships of descent. It was here that the methods of the earlier classifications came into their own. Because, in each case, a large number of characters had been examined, and one species compared with another in the sum total of characters, the whole system could be taken over as a series of evolutionary sequences. This however had disadvantages and led, and still leads, to excess of enthusiasm. Evolutionists often rushed into print with family trees and hypothetical ancestors far beyond the evidence available to them. Problems such as the origin of vertebrates or of insects spawned a huge literature based more on imagination than on facts.

Evidence for evolution comes from many sources but particularly from structure, development and, above all, from fossil history. But more phyla than not have either no fossil history at all or only a rudimentary one. In those few groups which do have a good fossil history, especially the vertebrates, the classification based on morphology of living forms has been greatly modified by the information from fossils, but in the rest the idea that our present classifications represent a true picture of actual lines of descent is based on little or no evidence. Most classifications, although often assumed today to represent descent, and in general probably doing so, are no more than refined versions of earlier ones based on morphological affinity. They always will be, even when genetic, physiological and biochemical information is available to a much greater extent than it is today.

If any classification is to give a true picture of relationship by descent, then any two or more categories at the same level in a hierarchy must all descend from ancestral species in their own line after such species have evolved from ancestors common to all the categories. A hierarchy of this sort is known as a **clade**. If, on the other hand, two or more groups at any given time, so far as we are concerned here, the present time, are set apart on good common characters, even though they are known from the fossil record not to be cladal in origin, such a classification is known as a **grade**.

The bony fish, as classified here, give a good example of grades. The infraclass Holostei contains the living forms *Amia*, the bowfin, and *Lepisosteus* the garpikes; its members have a number of characters in common which are not shared by members of the infraclass Teleostei, a group which contains almost all other living bony fishes. A third infraclass, the Chondrostei, which contains only the sturgeons and their relatives, are survivors of a primitive and early stock. If however we look at the known fossil record we find that the Teleostei were derived in the Jurassic, probably several times, from an ancestral stock of which *Amia* is the only other survivor; whilst the group to which *Lepisosteus* belongs has a continuous fossil record on its own back to the Permian and no known ancestor in common with *Amia*. The classification which puts *Amia* and *Lepisosteus* together is a gradal one. If we used a cladal one it would be necessary to put *Amia* with the teleosts and *Lepisosteus* by itself. Some palaeontologists would argue that the classification should be altered to a cladal one, but this would mean that it would have to be altered again and again as the origin of the teleosts and of the stock from which *Lepisosteus* comes became better known. The best answer to this difficulty is to stick to conservative classifications so far as possible, and to explain their limitations as an expression of descent.

Another difficulty is caused by the problem of convergent evolution. Animal species from unrelated stocks may evolve in such a way that they come to bear at least superficial resemblance to each other both in form and in habits. The Tasmanian wolf *Thylacinus* bears a resemblance in general form to wolves and dogs and is an active carnivore, hunting its prey by smell. But a slightly closer study will show that it is a marsupial with all the fundamental characters of the metatherian mammals, whereas true wolves and dogs are eutherian. But convergence is not always easy to spot. Until recently, cartilaginous and bony fishes were placed in a common class Pisces, and indeed in pre-Linnaean times the whales were included as well. It is now considered that the fusiform, fish-like shape is almost the only common character, other than those common to all vertebrates, and it may even be that the two groups were independently evolved from jawless ancestors.

The classification which is given here is concerned only with living animals, and it has been put together by general zoologists after consultation with specialists, particularly in those large groups in which there are varied opinions as to what is best. No two zoologists asked to prepare independent classifications would come up with the same answers, but the present one will certainly be comprehensible to all, although they may not agree with it. For example, the bony fish are treated in what some may think to be an out-of-date way, whilst the treatment of the insects may be thought new-fangled, because the primarily wingless orders are all excluded.

The treatment is intended for ecologists and other observers of nature in the wild, and consequently some groups have been treated in much more detail than others. Some have not been divided below phyla, but no phylum has been omitted, although one has had to be included as an addendum. All terrestrial vertebrates have been taken down as far as families, because these are the groups that field workers are most likely to encounter, and on which most ecological work has been done. It would have been useful to have treated the insects and the fishes in the same detail, but the very large number of families, perhaps a thousand in the insects, and the technical language required, precluded it. The amount of breakdown in each phylum is at the judgment of the compilers. The descriptions given of each group are not intended as a certain means of identifying its members but rather as a brief note on their general appearances and habits. Figures are given for the approximate numbers of described species in each group. In small groups these are close to the truth, but in large ones they are usually approximations and the available guesses often differ widely. An exception is found in the birds in which the total of about 8,500 is subject to little else than matters of opinion as to which should be treated as species and which as subspecies.

Finally a word of warning: the running headline at the top of each of the first few pages reads 'Invertebrates'. This term is one of convenience which has been used for a long time, but it is not a classificatory grouping. The various invertebrate phyla are not more closely related together than any one of them is to the vertebrates.

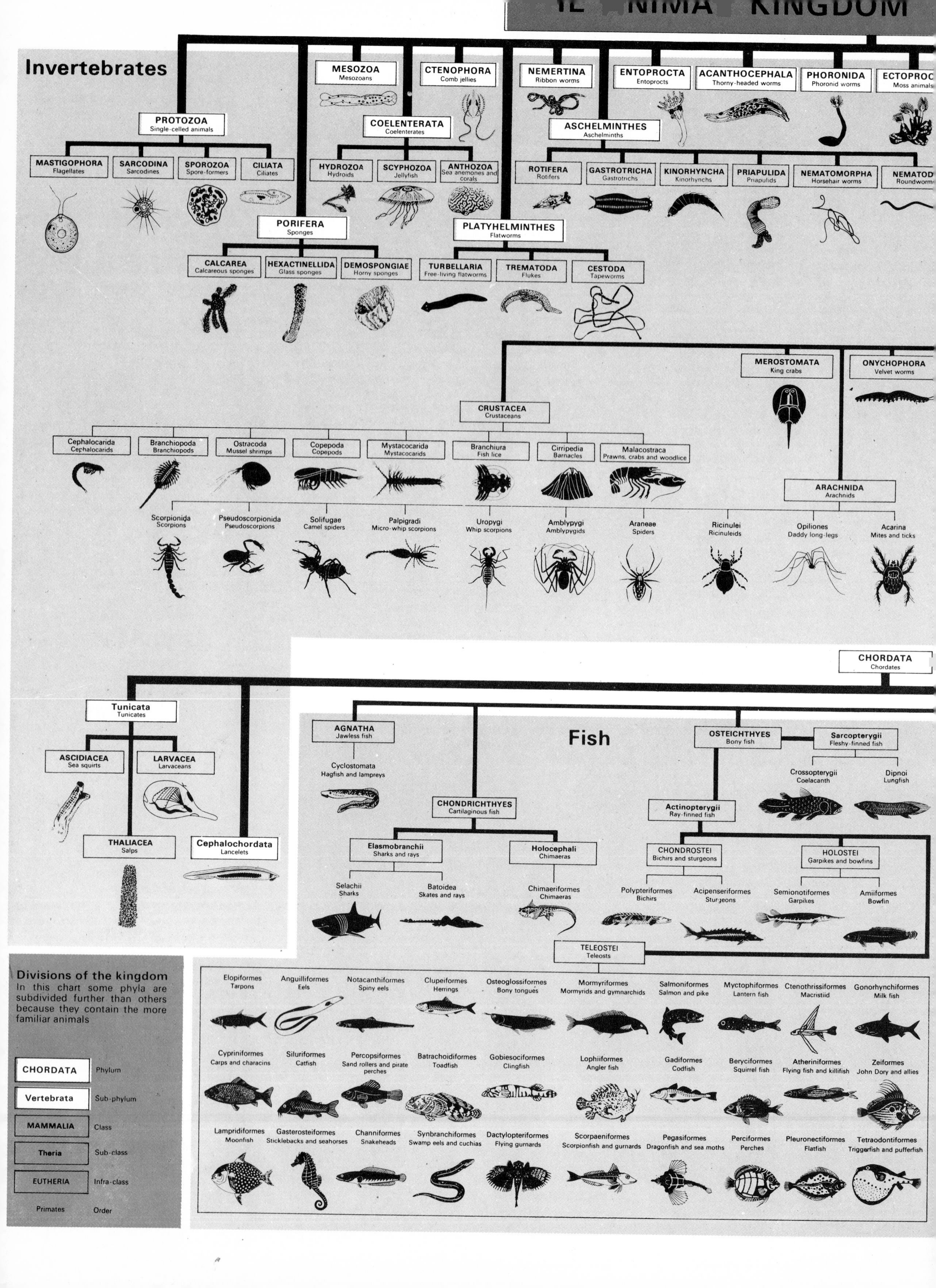

KINGDOM
Invertebrates
PROTOZOA
Single-celled animals
MASTIGOPHORA
Flagellates
SARCODINA
Sarcodines
SPOROZOA
Spore-formers
CILIATA
Ciliates
MESOZOA
Mesozoans
CTENOPHORA
Comb jellies
COELENTERATA
Coelenterates
HYDROZOA
Hydroids
SCYPHOZOA
Jellyfish
ANTHOZOA
Sea anemones and corals
PORIFERA
Sponges
CALCAREA
Calcareous sponges
HEXACTINELLIDA
Glass sponges
DEMOSPONGIAE
Horny sponges
NEMERTINA
Ribbon worms
ENTOPROCTA
Entoprocts
ACANTHOCEPHALA
Thorny-headed worms
PHORONIDA
Phoronid worms
ASCHELMINTHES
Aschelminths
ROTIFERA
Rotifers
GASTROTRICHA
Gastrotrichs
KINORHYNCHA
Kinorhynchs
PRIAPULIDA
Priapulids
NEMATOMORPHA
Horsehair worms
PLATYHELMINTHES
Flatworms
TURBELLARIA
Free-living flatworms
TREMATODA
Flukes
CESTODA
Tapeworms
MEROSTOMATA
King crabs
ONYCHOPHORA
Velvet worms
CRUSTACEA
Crustaceans
Cephalocarida
Cephalocarids
Branchiopoda
Branchiopods
Ostracoda
Mussel shrimps
Copepoda
Copepods
Mystacocarida
Mystacocarids
Branchiura
Fish lice
Cirripedia
Barnacles
Malacostraca
Prawns, crabs and woodlice
ARACHNIDA
Arachnids
Scorpionida
Scorpions
Pseudoscorpionida
Pseudoscorpions
Solifugae
Camel spiders
Palpigradi
Micro-whip scorpions
Uropygi
Whip scorpions
Amblypygi
Amblypygids
Araneae
Spiders
Ricinulei
Ricinuleids
Opiliones
Daddy long-legs
Acarina
Mites and ticks
CHORDATA
Chordates
Tunicata
Tunicates
ASCIDIACEA
Sea squirts
LARVACEA
Larvaceans
THALIACEA
Salps
Cephalochordata
Lancelets
Fish
AGNATHA
Jawless fish
Cyclostomata
Hagfish and lampreys
CHONDRICHTHYES
Cartilaginous fish
Elasmobranchii
Sharks and rays
Selachii
Sharks
Batoidea
Skates and rays
Holocephali
Chimaeras
Chimaeriformes
Chimaeras
OSTEICHTHYES
Bony fish
Sarcopterygii
Fleshy-finned fish
Crossopterygii
Coelacanth
Dipnoi
Lungfish
Actinopterygii
Ray-finned fish
CHONDROSTEI
Bichirs and sturgeons
Polypteriformes
Bichirs
Acipenseriformes
Sturgeons
HOLOSTEI
Garpikes and bowfins
Semionotiformes
Garpikes
Amiiformes
Bowfin
TELEOSTEI
Teleosts
Elopiformes
Tarpons
Anguilliformes
Eels
Notacanthiformes
Spiny eels
Clupeiformes
Herrings
Osteoglossiformes
Bony tongues
Mormyriformes
Mormyrids and gymnarchids
Salmoniformes
Salmon and pike
Myctophiformes
Lantern fish
Ctenothrissiformes
Macristiid
Gonorhynchiformes
Milk fish
Cypriniformes
Carps and characins
Siluriformes
Catfish
Percopsiformes
Sand rollers and pirate perches
Batrachoidiformes
Toadfish
Gobiesociformes
Clingfish
Lophiiformes
Angler fish
Gadiformes
Codfish
Beryciformes
Squirrel fish
Atheriniformes
Flying fish and killifish
Zeiformes
John Dory and allies
Lampridiformes
Moonfish
Gasterosteiformes
Sticklebacks and seahorses
Channiformes
Snakeheads
Synbranchiformes
Swamp eels and cuchias
Dactylopteriformes
Flying gurnards
Scorpaeniformes
Scorpionfish and gurnards
Pegasiformes
Dragonfish and sea moths
Perciformes
Perches
Pleuronectiformes
Flatfish
Tetraodontiformes
Triggerfish and pufferfish
Divisions of the kingdom
In this chart some phyla are subdivided further than others because they contain the more familiar animals
CHORDATA
Phylum
Vertebrata
Sub-phylum
MAMMALIA
Class
Theria
Sub-class
EUTHERIA
Infra-class
Primates
Order

The simplest division of the living world is into the plant and animal kingdoms, though some simple organisms, such as viruses, do not fit conveniently into either. Animals are broadly distinguished from plants by being capable of independent movement and by needing to feed on other living matter, either plant or animal

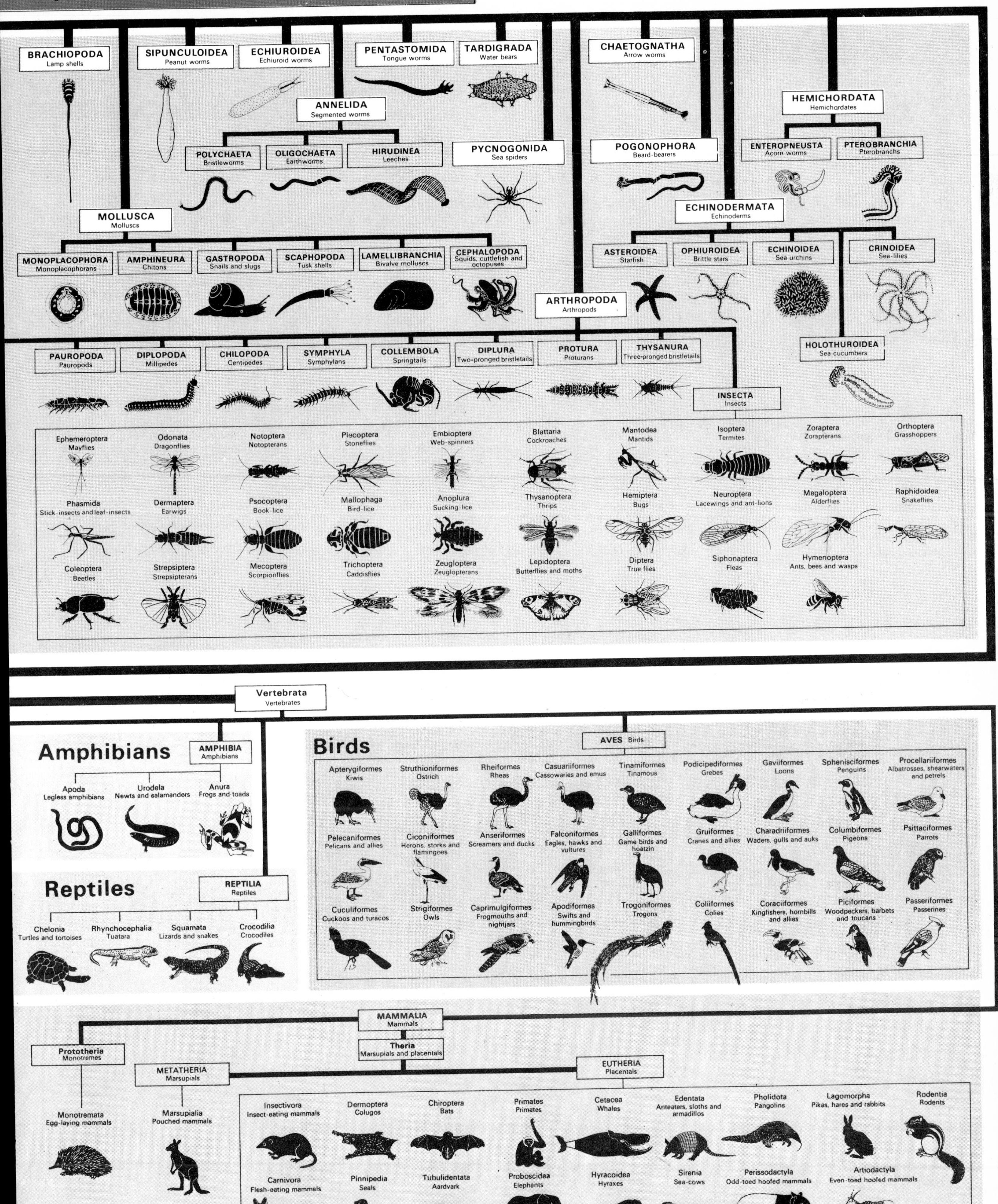

Mammals

Invertebrates

Sizes of invertebrates: measurements are overall lengths unless otherwise stated

The word invertebrates, meaning animals without backbones, is used to describe 95 per cent of the species in the animal kingdom in order to differentiate them from the remaining 5 per cent—the vertebrates, or animals with backbones. Man gives this importance to vertebrates mainly because he is a vertebrate himself. But the invertebrates vastly outnumber the vertebrates, both in species and individuals, and they show a greater variety of forms.

PHYLUM PROTOZOA

Single-celled animals; more than 30,000 species

Protozoans are animals of the simplest type, consisting of only one complex and often specialised cell. In some cases the distinction between the plant and animal kingdoms is difficult to define, and some protozoans produce their own food in the same way as plants, by photosynthesis. Most of the thousands of species are microscopic, but some are ¼ in. long. There are four classes:

CLASS MASTIGOPHORA

Flagellates

The free-living or parasitic organisms in this class have at least one flagellum—a long, whip-like fibre which beats in such a way that the animal is pushed forward. In some species cells are grouped together to form a colony. Reproduction is usually by binary fission—the division of the animal into two or more daughter cells of equal size; in some species a sexual process involving the fusion of reproductive cells occurs. Example:

Chlamydomonas angulosa: found world-wide in fresh waters. It has plant-like cell walls and produces its food by photosynthesis—the process by which carbon dioxide and water are combined into carbohydrates, using the energy of sunlight

CLASS SARCODINA

Sarcodines

These protozoans have mobile extensions of the body called pseudopodia, which are used for capturing prey. Members of the group that move about actively also use them for locomotion. Sarcodines are either parasitic or free-living in water or damp soil. They reproduce by binary fission or by a sexual process involving the fusion of reproductive cells. Some forms bear flagella at certain stages of their lives. Examples:

Amoeba proteus (diameter 0·02 in.): found in fresh waters everywhere, it is the most widely known protozoan. It varies in shape as new pseudopodia are formed, and the cell contains a nucleus and tiny membrane packages called vacuoles, one for food and one which fills with water and then expels it to regulate the body's water content

Actinophrys sol: one of the heliozoans, or 'sun animalcules', it is found everywhere in fresh waters. It has pseudopodia stiffened with silica—a mineral present in many types of stone—projecting all round the cell. Some members of this group secrete a shell of silica, and the ooze covering the bed of warm, deep oceans often consists of a multitude of these shells deposited over millions of years

CLASS SPOROZOA

Spore-formers

These parasitic organisms are simple in structure and, like many parasites, have complex life cycles with several distinct generations and often more than one host. At some stages they increase very rapidly by multiple division of the cell. Example:

Plasmodium vivax: formerly widespread but now uncommon in civilised areas. It is spread by mosquitoes of the genus *Anopheles* and causes benign tertian malaria in man; the malaria parasites attack the red blood corpuscles, and produce fever and weakness as side-effects. The victim suffers a paroxysm (chills and fever) every 48 hours. The fevers usually occur every other day for several weeks, slowly decreasing in severity, and may start anew several weeks afterwards

CLASS CILIATA

Ciliates

These protozoans, some of which are parasitic, have many tiny, short, lash-like extensions called cilia and at least two nuclei, one large and one or more smaller. They reproduce asexually by binary fission and sexually by conjugation, which involves the temporary joining together of two individuals to exchange nuclear material. Example:

Paramecium caudatum: common in fresh waters everywhere, it moves by means of its cilia and feeds on small particles of organic matter taken in at a special receptive point

PHYLUM PORIFERA

Sponges; about 5000 species

Sponges probably evolved a multicellular structure independently of other multi-celled animals, the metazoans. The cells, grouped together so as to produce a network of chambers connected both to one another and to the exterior, are of different types. They include some irregularly shaped cells which move in amoeba-like fashion and secrete mineral fibres called spicules which strengthen the sponges, and others called collar-cells, which bear a flagellum. Oxygen and small particles of food are drawn into the sponge through the pores by the beating of the flagella. Most sponges are marine but some inhabit fresh water. Reproduction is either sexual or asexual. In the case of asexual reproduction, small groups of cells enclosed in a horny coat are budded off. There are three classes:

CLASS CALCAREA

Calcareous sponges

These sponges have no jelly-like substance between the cells, and their supporting skeleton is composed of chalk (calcium carbonate) spicules. These are either single and straight or have three or four branches. Example:

Leucosolenia botryoides: inhabits shallow coastal waters of the Atlantic

CLASS HEXACTINELLIDA

Glass sponges

These sponges also have no jelly-like substance between the cells, but their skeleton is composed of spicules of silica. In this case, each of the spicules has six branches. Some spicules are often fused to form a lattice structure, giving the sponge a glass-like appearance when dried. Example:

Venus's flower basket *Euplectella aspergillum*: lives in deep seas. It has a white filmy skeleton and a tuft of long spicules holding its body away from the mud of the sea floor

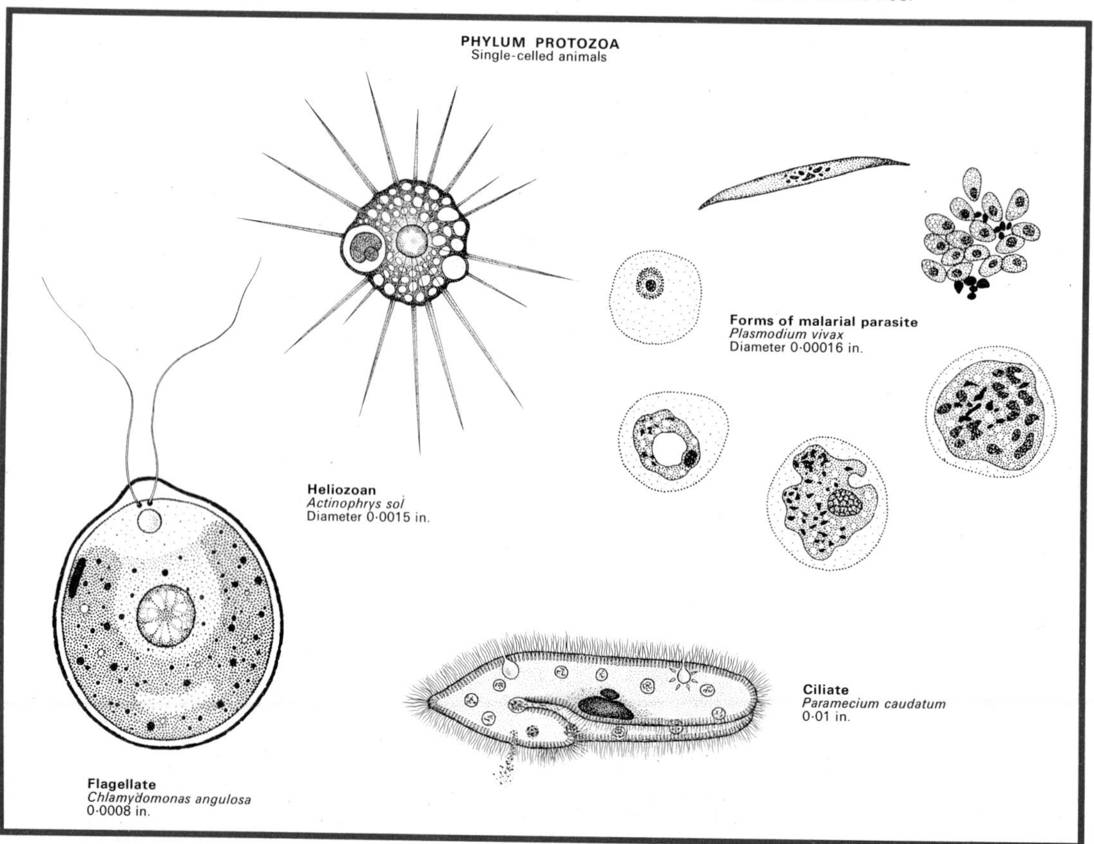

Periodic Classification

Including some approximate atomic weights

Period																		
1	1 H Hydrogen 1																	2 He Helium 4
2	3 Li Lithium 7	4 Be Beryllium 9											5 B Boron 11	6 C Carbon 12	7 N Nitrogen 14	8 O Oxygen 16	9 F Fluorine 19	10 Ne Neon 20
3	11 Na Sodium 23	12 Mg Magnesium 24											13 Al Aluminium 27	14 Si Silicon 28	15 P Phosphorus 31	16 S Sulphur 32	17 Cl Chlorine 35·5	18 Ar Argon 40
4	19 K Potassium 39	20 Ca Calcium 40	21 Sc Scandium	22 Ti Titanium	23 V Vanadium	24 Cr Chromium 52	25 Mn Manganese 55	26 Fe Iron 56	27 Co Cobalt 59	28 Ni Nickel 59	29 Cu Copper 63·5	30 Zn Zinc 65	31 Ga Gallium	32 Ge Germanium	33 As Arsenic 75	34 Se Selenium	35 Br Bromine 80	36 Kr Krypton 84
5	37 Rb Rubidium	38 Sr Strontium 88	39 Y Yttrium	40 Zr Zirconium	41 Nb Niobium	42 Mo Molybdenum	43 Tc Technetium	44 Ru Ruthenium	45 Rh Rhodium	46 Pd Palladium	47 Ag Silver 108	48 Cd Cadmium 112	49 In Indium	50 Sn Tin 119	51 Sb Antimony 122	52 Te Tellurium	53 I Iodine 127	54 Xe Xenon 131
6	55 Cs Caesium	56 Ba Barium 137	57 La Lanthanum *	72 Hf Hafnium	73 Ta Tantalum	74 W Tungsten	75 Re Rhenium	76 Os Osmium	77 Ir Iridium	78 Pt Platinum 195	79 Au Gold 197	80 Hg Mercury 201	81 Tl Thallium	82 Pb Lead 207	83 Bi Bismuth 209	84 Po Polonium	85 At Astatine	86 Rn Radon
7	87 Fr Francium	88 Ra Radium	89 Ac Actinium †															

*58–71 Lanthanum series

†90–103 Actinium series

ICI

Published by

The Kynoch Press Limited
Thames House North
Millbank
London SW1P 4QG
Telephone: 01-834 4444

Designed by ICI Publicity Services Dept
Printed in England at The Kynoch Press Limited,
Birmingham B6 7ER

PHYLUM PORIFERA	Sponges
PHYLUM MESOZOA	Mesozoans
PHYLUM COELENTERATA	Jellyfish, sea anemones, corals
PHYLUM CTENOPHORA	Comb jellies
PHYLUM PLATYHELMINTHES	Flatworms

CLASS DEMOSPONGIAE

Horny sponges

All members of this class have a jelly-like substance between the cells, and a skeleton consisting of spicules of silica, or of a horny substance called spongin, or of a combination of silica spicules and spongin. They vary greatly in shape and size. Those with spicules have straight or four-branched ones. Example:

Bath sponge *Euspongia mollissima*: inhabits warm seas, including the Mediterranean and the Caribbean. The dead skeleton, rich in spongin, forms the bathroom sponge

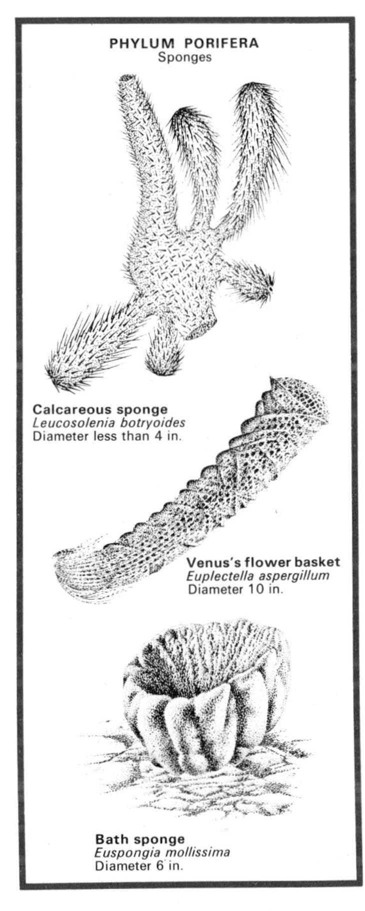

PHYLUM PORIFERA
Sponges

Calcareous sponge
Leucosolenia botryoides
Diameter less than 4 in.

Venus's flower basket
Euplectella aspergillum
Diameter 10 in.

Bath sponge
Euspongia mollissima
Diameter 6 in.

PHYLUM MESOZOA

Mesozoans; 50 species

This is a small and obscure group of parasites whose slender bodies consist of more than one cell, although the total number is small. Unlike most other multicellular animals, they lack distinct layers of cells and may not be related to them. They are simple in structure, but have a complex life cycle which includes a single-celled amoeba-like phase. Example:

Pseudicyema truncatum: a microscopic parasite in cuttlefish

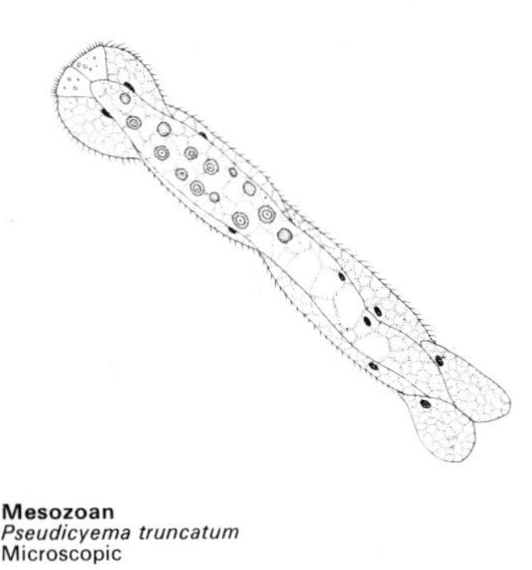

Mesozoan
Pseudicyema truncatum
Microscopic

PHYLUM COELENTERATA

Hydroids, jellyfish, sea anemones and corals

The members of this purely aquatic group, the most primitive of the true multi-celled animals, have radially symmetrical bodies with two layers of cells surrounding a body cavity which opens to the outside at one end to form a mouth. The mouth is fringed by tentacles bearing cells which can seize, sting and paralyse prey. There are two different structural types: the slender cylindrical polyps attached to rocks or other stationary objects, and the umbrella-shaped, free-swimming medusae. Some coelenterates pass through both forms during their life cycle. Polyps typically reproduce asexually by budding, in which a new animal is formed as an outgrowth of the parent polyp and the division of the animal into two is unequal. Medusae always reproduce sexually. There are three classes:

CLASS HYDROZOA

Hydroids; 2700 species

Typical hydroids pass through both polyp and medusa phases in their life cycle, but some species live only as polyps. Hydroids are small, inconspicuous creatures, measuring only a fraction of an inch, and much of the marine growth on rocks and shells is produced by hydroid polyps. Example:

Obelia geniculata: a colonial hydroid found in seas all over the world. Each colony consists of branching polyps protected by an external covering made of a skeletal material called chitin

CLASS SCYPHOZOA

Jellyfish; 200 species

The medusa phase is the dominant part of the life cycle of jellyfish, although there is also a smaller, stationary polyp stage. Most jellyfish are found in coastal waters. Example:

Common jellyfish *Aurelia aurita*: found in all parts of the world

CLASS ANTHOZOA

Sea anemones and corals; 6500 species

Anthozoans are either solitary or colonial animals in which there is no medusa phase. The digestive cavity of the polyp is divided by sheets of tissue bearing stinging cells on their edges. Corals are polyps protected by a hard external skeleton composed of calcium carbonate, which forms the material normally thought of as coral. Accumulations of coral in warm shallow seas form coral reefs. Example:

Brain coral *Meandrina cerebriformis*: its shape suggests the cerebral hemispheres of the human brain—a zigzag pattern of troughs separated by skeletal ridges. A colony of brain coral can measure up to 4 ft in diameter

PHYLUM CTENOPHORA

Comb jellies or sea walnuts; about 100 species

Like hydroids, comb jellies have two layers of cells, but they do not exist as either polyps or medusae. Most of them are round, and they live in surface waters, swimming by means of cilia. Some have a pair of tentacles bearing adhesive cells which produce a sticky secretion used in catching the small floating animals on which the comb jellies feed. Example:

Sea gooseberry *Pleurobrachia pileus*: common in the Atlantic Ocean. It is phosphorescent

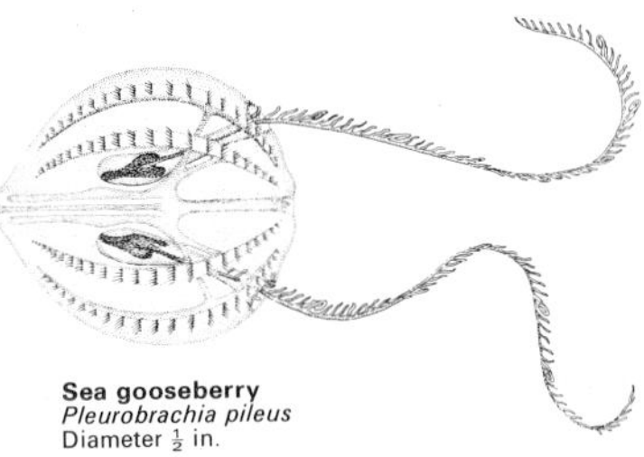

Sea gooseberry
Pleurobrachia pileus
Diameter $\frac{1}{2}$ in.

PHYLUM PLATYHELMINTHES

Flatworms

These flattened, worm-like animals are unsegmented and have no true body cavity. Both male and female reproductive organs occur in one individual and they reproduce both sexually and asexually. Some are free-living and others are parasites. In free-living forms the cell-layer called the ectoderm is ciliated. There are three classes:

CLASS TURBELLARIA

Free-living flatworms; 1600 species

Most of these flatworms are aquatic and live at the bottom of the sea or fresh waters in sand or mud, under stones and shells or on seaweed. They are usually less than 1 in. long. Example:

Dugesia tigrina: a carnivorous form common in fresh water. Like many of this group, it has remarkable powers of regeneration of lost parts of the body

CLASS TREMATODA

Flukes; 2400 species

These parasitic worms are oval to elongated in shape and vary in length from 0·04 in. to 23 ft. Fish are their main hosts. They reproduce sexually. Example:

Schistosoma haematobium: infects the veins of the bladders of humans in Africa and eastern Europe

CLASS CESTODA

Tapeworms; 1500 species

Tapeworms are parasites living in the gut of vertebrates. They are usually long, some reaching 40 ft. Example:

Taenia solium: a tapeworm which is parasitic in man. A hooked front end enables the worm to attach itself to the wall of the intestine and absorb digested food through its surface. It appears to be segmented, but each section is a complete individual, with its own reproductive system. Under-cooked pork is a source of infection

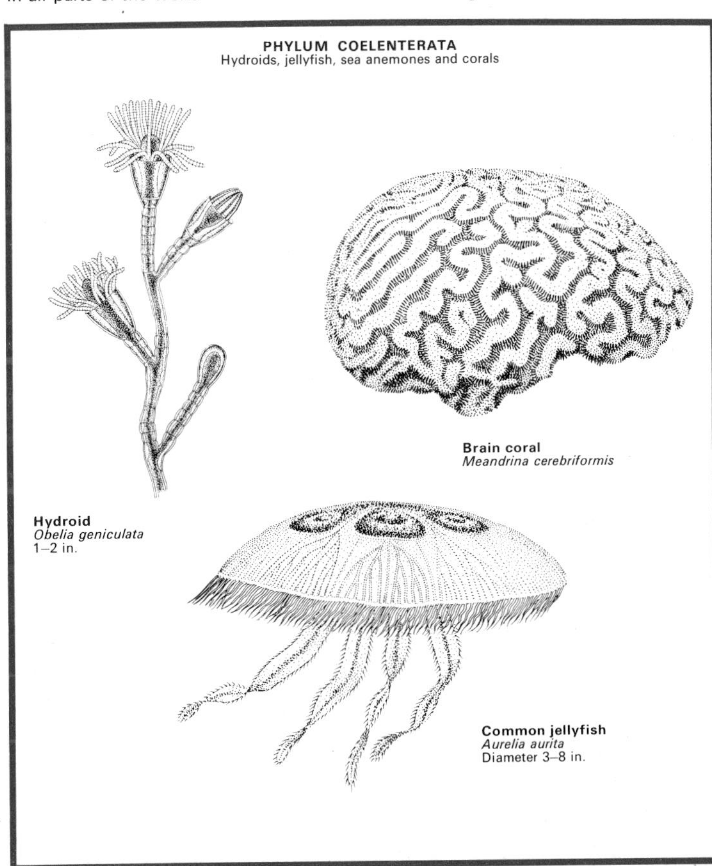

PHYLUM COELENTERATA
Hydroids, jellyfish, sea anemones and corals

Hydroid
Obelia geniculata
1–2 in.

Brain coral
Meandrina cerebriformis

Common jellyfish
Aurelia aurita
Diameter 3–8 in.

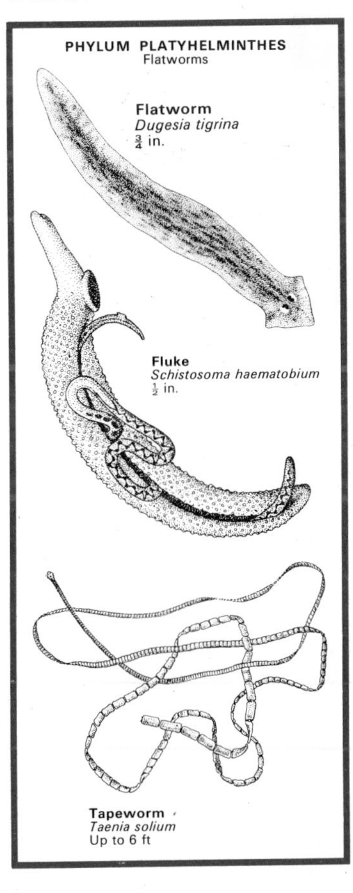

PHYLUM PLATYHELMINTHES
Flatworms

Flatworm
Dugesia tigrina
$\frac{3}{4}$ in.

Fluke
Schistosoma haematobium
$\frac{1}{2}$ in.

Tapeworm
Taenia solium
Up to 6 ft

PHYLUM NEMERTINA	Ribbon worms	PHYLUM ECTOPROCTA	Moss animals
PHYLUM ASCHELMINTHES	Aschelminths	PHYLUM PHORONIDA	Phoronids
PHYLUM ENTOPROCTA	Entoprocts	PHYLUM BRACHIOPODA	Lamp shells
PHYLUM ACANTHOCEPHALA	Thorny-headed worms	PHYLUM MOLLUSCA	Molluscs

PHYLUM NEMERTINA

Ribbon worms; 750 species
Like flatworms, the ribbon worms are long and flattened. They lack a body cavity, are unsegmented and have an outer layer covered with cilia. Unlike flatworms, they have an alimentary canal opening to the outside at the mouth and the anus. The sexes are always separate. Some species of ribbon worms are more than 60 ft long. Most inhabit shallow seas and coastal waters. Example:
Tubulanus annulatus: frequently dredged from shallow waters around European coasts

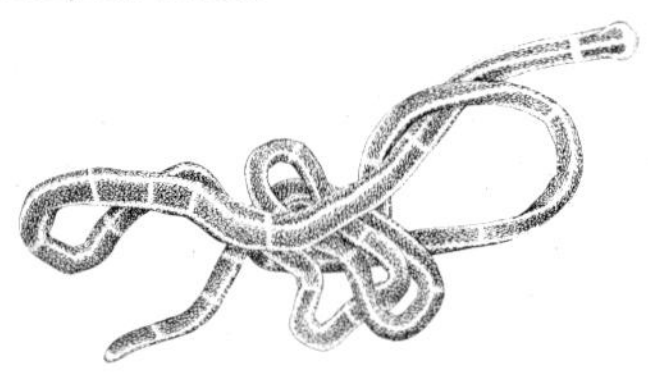

Ribbon worm
Tubulanus annulatus
Up to 20 in.

PHYLUM ASCHELMINTHES

Aschelminths
This is a group of unsegmented animals having, like the ribbon worms, an alimentary canal with both a mouth and an anus. The cavity in the body round the gut is not a true body cavity. There are six classes:

CLASS ROTIFERA

Rotifers; 1500 species
All rotifers are microscopic—few exceed 0·02 in. in length—and live in fresh water. Their bodies are usually transparent, but some appear to be delicately coloured. Some elongated forms live in mud at the bottom of ponds; other more rounded forms are free-swimming; and others are stationary. A ring of thread-like cilia round the mouth provides the propulsion for swimming, where this occurs, and creates water currents which convey food to the animal. Reproduction is sexual and the sexes are separate. In most cases, male rotifers are very much smaller than the females. Example:
Hydatina senta: found world wide. The male measures 0·005 in.; the female 0·01 in.

CLASS GASTROTRICHA

Gastrotrichs; 175 species
These are marine and freshwater animals similar to rotifers. Example:
Chaetonotus brevispinosus: found on the bottoms of lakes, ponds and streams

CLASS KINORHYNCHA

Kinorhynchs; 100 species
The kinorhynchs resemble the gastrotrichs but are exclusively marine. Example:
Echinoderes dujardiniis: lives in the muddy bottoms of coastal waters

CLASS PRIAPULIDA

Priapulids; 8 species
These cucumber-shaped animals live in muddy bottoms of coastal waters of the colder parts of the oceans. Example:
Priapulus bicaudatus: found in mud in cold coastal waters

CLASS NEMATOMORPHA

Horsehair worms; 225 species
These long slender worms are parasitic in insects and crustaceans when juvenile, but inhabit damp soil or water when adult. Example:
Gordius aquaticus: lives in fresh water when adult

CLASS NEMATODA

Roundworms; over 10,000 species
All roundworms are similar in appearance, with long bodies, pointed at each end, covered by a thick horny layer, or cuticle. There are parasitic species and species which live in soil, fresh water and the sea. The smallest are microscopic and the largest is about 40 in. long. The sexes are usually separate. Example:
Ascaris lumbricoides: found world wide, it is a common parasite of mammals such as pigs, and sometimes of man

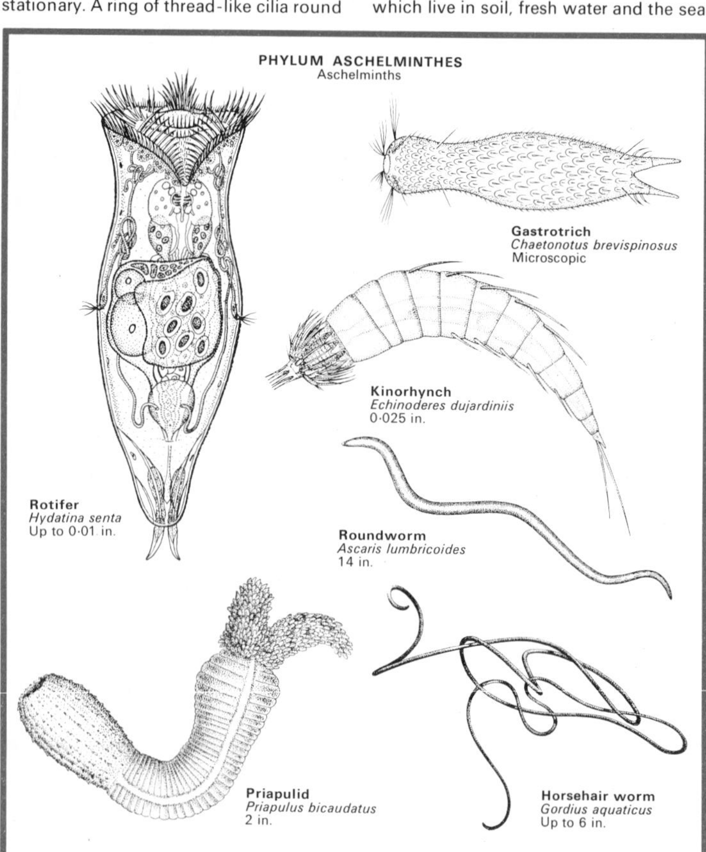

PHYLUM ASCHELMINTHES
Aschelminths

Rotifer
Hydatina senta
Up to 0·01 in.

Gastrotrich
Chaetonotus brevispinosus
Microscopic

Kinorhynch
Echinoderes dujardiniis
0·025 in.

Roundworm
Ascaris lumbricoides
14 in.

Priapulid
Priapulus bicaudatus
2 in.

Horsehair worm
Gordius aquaticus
Up to 6 in.

PHYLUM ENTOPROCTA

Entoprocts; 60 species
Entoprocts are rather similar in appearance to hydroid polyps, but possess an alimentary canal with both the mouth and the anus situated within a ring of stingless tentacles. A chalky external skeleton supports and protects the body. Most of the species inhabit the seashore or shallow seas. Example:
Loxosoma saltans: widely distributed on European, American and Asian coasts

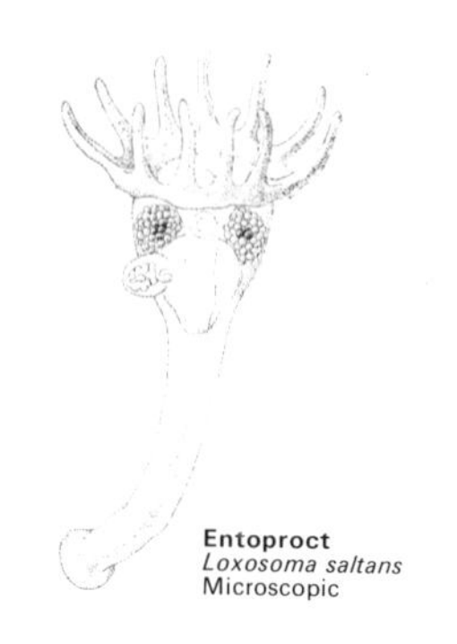

Entoproct
Loxosoma saltans
Microscopic

PHYLUM ACANTHOCEPHALA

Thorny-headed worms; 300 species
These are parasitic worms which attach themselves to the host by means of a proboscis with curved spines. Otherwise they are very like nematode worms; they range from less than 1 in. long to about 20 in. Typical hosts are waterfowl which become infected by eating freshwater shrimps which harbour the larvae. Example:
Neoechinorhynchus rutili: a widespread species. The larva attaches itself to the intestines of a vertebrate which has eaten a crustacean harbouring it

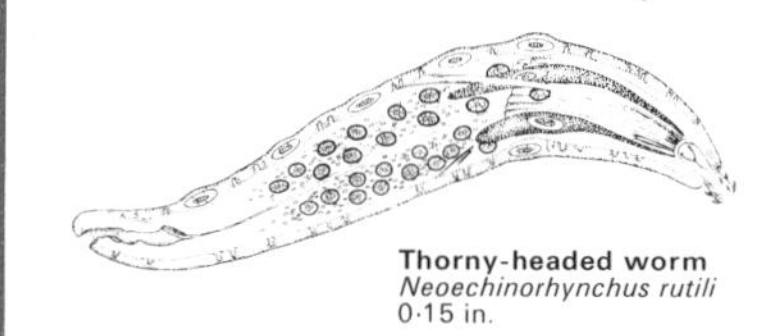

Thorny-headed worm
Neoechinorhynchus rutili
0·15 in.

PHYLUM ECTOPROCTA

Moss animals; about 4000 species
The horny or chalky external cases of these small, colonial, mainly marine animals are branching and are often mistaken for small seaweeds. They possess a lophophore, a horseshoe-shaped fold of the body wall encircling the mouth. Ciliated tentacles round the mouth carry food particles through the gut. Ectoprocts are hermaphrodites and reproduction is both asexual and sexual. Example:
Lophopus crystallinus: a freshwater species with a horny case

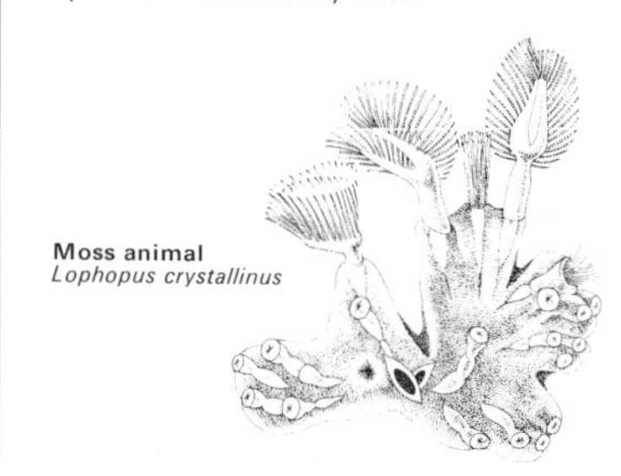

Moss animal
Lophopus crystallinus

PHYLUM PHORONIDA

Phoronids; about 15 species
These marine, tube-dwelling animals, like the moss animals, have ciliated tentacles situated on a lophophore. The cilia on the tentacles drive a current of water through the lophophore and plankton is collected in the process. Example:
Phoronis architecta: lives buried in sand near the low water mark

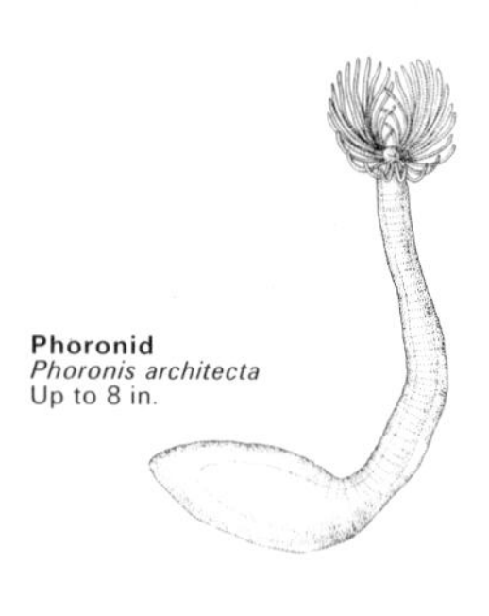

Phoronid
Phoronis architecta
Up to 8 in.

PHYLUM BRACHIOPODA

Lamp shells; about 260 species
These exclusively marine animals are enclosed in a shell and bear a superficial resemblance to molluscs such as clams. Molluscs' shells, however, are placed one on each side of the body, while those of brachiopods cover the upper and lower surfaces of the animals. Typically, lamp shells have ciliated tentacles borne on a lophophore, a true body cavity and, in some forms, a muscular stalk. Reproduction is sexual, and the sexes are usually separate. Example:
Lingula unguis: found in the Pacific from Japan to Queensland, living in vertical burrows in sand and mud. This species belongs to a genus which appears to be very ancient—living forms exactly resemble fossil forms of 500 million years ago

Lamp shell
Lingula unguis
Diameter 4–5 in.

PHYLUM MOLLUSCA

Molluscs
These unsegmented animals, with body cavities and highly developed blood and nervous systems, live on land, in fresh water and in the sea. The body is divided into a head, a muscular foot and a humped back covered by a mantle of skin which is folded to form a cavity used as a lung in some forms. This mantle usually secretes the animal's chalky shell. Molluscs do not have a standard shape, and in an evolutionary sense they are plastic material. The outlines of the body are freely altered as new habits are acquired and new structures are needed. Most molluscs are slow-moving. Reproduction is sexual; the sexes are separate in some species, and others are hermaphroditic. There are six classes:

PHYLUM MOLLUSCA	Molluscs
PHYLUM SIPUNCULOIDEA	Peanut worms
PHYLUM ECHIUROIDEA	Echiuroid worms
PHYLUM ANNELIDA	Segmented worms
PHYLUM PENTASTOMIDA	Tongue worms

CLASS MONOPLACOPHORA

Monoplacophs; 2 species

This class contains the most primitive surviving molluscs. They are superficially like limpets, but differ in that the two sides of the body are symmetrical and in having more organs such as kidneys and gills. This indicates that molluscs might have been originally derived from segmented animals. Example:

Neopilina galatheae: the first surviving member of this group to be discovered, it was dredged up from the depths of the Pacific in 1952. It has a flat, saucer-shaped shell, with a ventral foot, a mouth in front and anus behind. Five pairs of gills lie in shallow grooves between the mantle skirt and the foot

CLASS AMPHINEURA

Chitons; 1150 species

The elongated and bilaterally symmetrical chitons are primitive molluscs, lacking both tentacles and eyes. A broad, flat foot enables them to adhere to rocks and shells. Example:

Chiton tuberculatus : found on West Indian coasts

CLASS GASTROPODA

Slugs, snails and limpets; more than 35,000 species

The members of this large group have both tentacles and eyes. The visceral mass is horizontally twisted through 180°, so that the body is not symmetrical. There is a single shell, but in some forms the shell is very small or absent altogether. A typical shell is a conical spire composed of tubular whorls. All the land molluscs belong to this group, as well as many aquatic gastropods. Example:

Edible or **Roman snail** *Helix pomatia*: a plant-eating land snail of continental Europe

CLASS SCAPHOPODA

Tusk shells; about 200 species

These small marine animals live in sand under deep water. They have tubular shells, and feet adapted for burrowing and long, thin projections growing from the head which bear suckers used to seize food. Example:

Dentalium entalis: lives on sandy North Atlantic coasts

CLASS LAMELLIBRANCHIA

Bivalve molluscs; 8000 species

Members of this large group of flattened molluscs have rounded, oval or elongated shells, and a mantle divided into two lobes, each secreting half of the shell, which is hinged over the animal's back. The large gills strain small food particles from water swept in by movement of the thread-like cilia. There are sedentary and slow-moving forms, many of which are adapted for burrowing. Example:

Common mussel *Mytilus edulis*: clamps itself to rocks by means of sticky threads

CLASS CEPHALOPODA

Squids, cuttlefish and octopuses; about 700 species

These are the most highly evolved of the molluscs, some possessing a very efficient nervous system and eyes. The two sides of the body are symmetrical, and the well-developed head is surrounded by a circle of sucker-bearing arms. Water leaves the mantle cavity through a muscular tubular organ called a siphon, derived from the foot. The shell is often almost invisible or entirely absent. The only surviving genus with a complete external shell is *Nautilus*. Example:

Common octopus *Octopus vulgaris*: lives at the bottom of shallow, warm seas and feeds largely on crabs

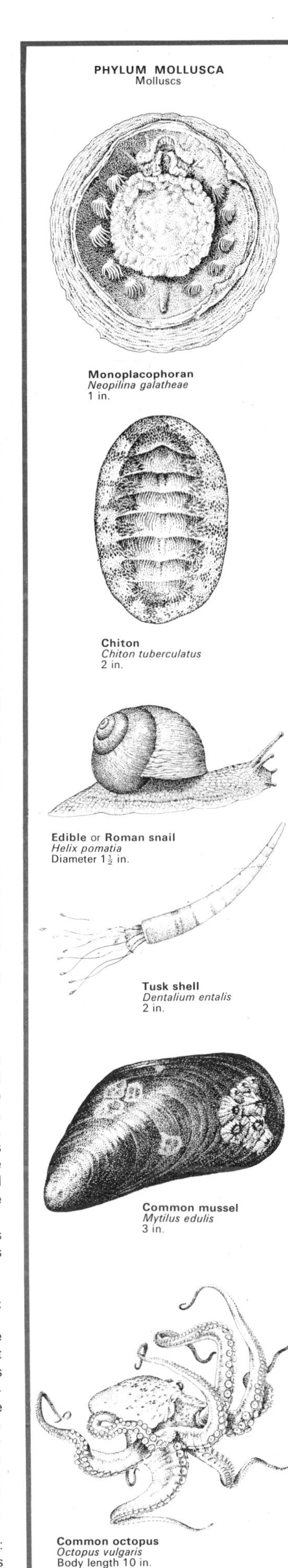

PHYLUM MOLLUSCA
Molluscs

Monoplacophoran
Neopilina galatheae
1 in.

Chiton
Chiton tuberculatus
2 in.

Edible or **Roman snail**
Helix pomatia
Diameter 1½ in.

Tusk shell
Dentalium entalis
2 in.

Common mussel
Mytilus edulis
3 in.

Common octopus
Octopus vulgaris
Body length 10 in.

PHYLUM SIPUNCULOIDEA

Peanut worms; about 250 species

The exclusively marine peanut worms have a well-developed body cavity, but are apparently unsegmented. The forepart of the body can be tucked into the plumper part immediately behind. The animals of this phylum are generally sedentary, living in burrows in sand. Reproduction is sexual and the sexes are separate. Example:

Dendrostomum pyroides : burrows in sand and mud on the west coast of North America

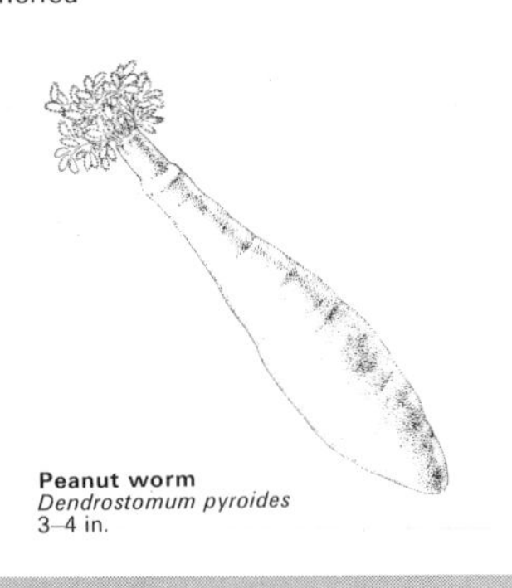

Peanut worm
Dendrostomum pyroides
3–4 in.

PHYLUM ECHIUROIDEA

Echiuroid worms; about 60 species

These unsegmented marine worms have one or more pairs of bristles similar to those of annelid worms, to which they are probably related. The characteristic mobile proboscis cannot be introduced into the mouth. Most echiuroid worms live in sand or rock crevices, intertidally or in shallow water. Example:

Genus *Echiurus* : live in U-shaped, mucus-lined burrows. The mobile proboscis traps particles of food from the sand surface which are brought to the mouth by thread-like cilia

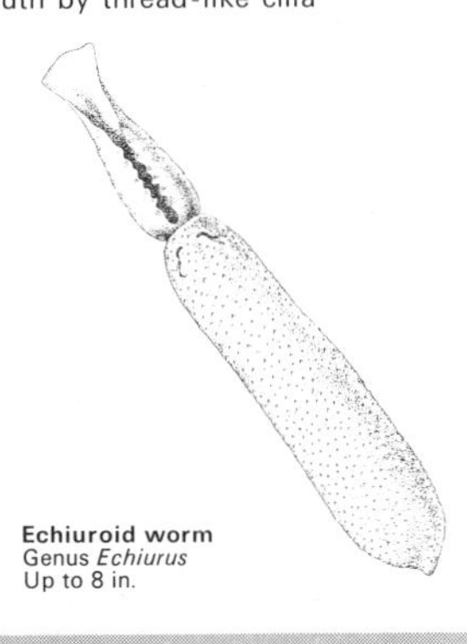

Echiuroid worm
Genus *Echiurus*
Up to 8 in.

PHYLUM ANNELIDA

Segmented worms

The worms in this group have bodies divided into similar parts, or segments, and the muscular body of each segment is covered with a thin cuticle from which segmentally arranged bristles, or chaetae, protrude. The head contains the brain; the body cavity surrounds the alimentary canal; and the nerve cord runs along the underside of the body. There are three classes:

CLASS POLYCHAETA

Bristle worms; over 4000 species

These marine annelid worms have numerous bristles growing from muscular, fleshy, paddle-like appendages called parapodia. They are either free-moving or sedentary, and vary greatly in structure and way of life. The sexes are usually separate. Example:

Green ragworm *Nereis virens*: an Atlantic species. It is an active burrower, swimmer and predator

CLASS OLIGOCHAETA

Earthworms; over 2500 species

These worms have fewer bristles than the bristle worms and they lack parapodia. All are hermaphrodites, but they usually have a complex reproductive system which eliminates the possibility of self-fertilisation. They range in length from a few inches to more than 10 ft. Example:

Common earthworm *Lumbricus terrestris*: found in the Northern Hemisphere. It feeds by swallowing soil and digesting particles of organic matter contained in it

CLASS HIRUDINEA

Leeches; more than 300 species

These parasitic annelids have relatively few segments, a greatly reduced body cavity, and neither bristles nor parapodia. They have suckers at both ends of the body with which they cling to their hosts, plants or animals, feeding on sap or blood. They breed in a similar complex way to earthworms and most species are found in water. Example:

European medicinal leech *Hirudo medicinalis*: formerly used in medicine to suck blood

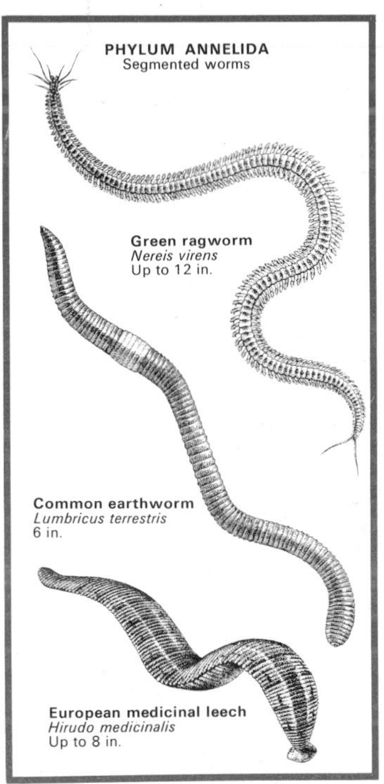

PHYLUM ANNELIDA
Segmented worms

Green ragworm
Nereis virens
Up to 12 in.

Common earthworm
Lumbricus terrestris
6 in.

European medicinal leech
Hirudo medicinalis
Up to 8 in.

PHYLUM PENTASTOMIDA

Tongue worms; about 70 species

These worms, found in the lungs and nasal passages of vertebrates, are covered by a thick cuticle which is shed periodically. They have no circulatory or respiratory systems. Tongue worms occur mostly in the tropics. Example:

Cephalobaena tetrapoda : found in the lungs of tropical snakes

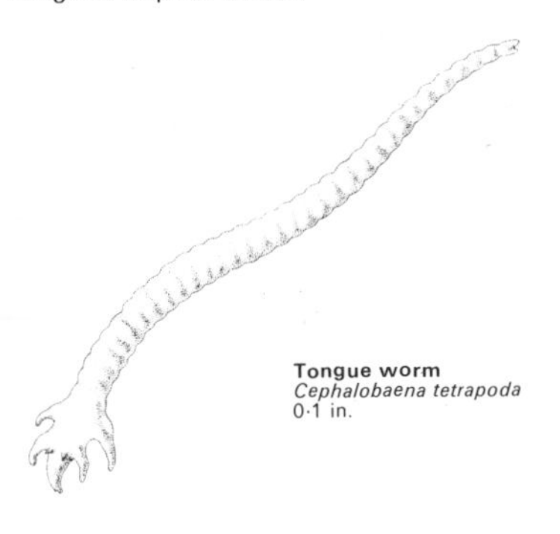

Tongue worm
Cephalobaena tetrapoda
0·1 in.

Invertebrates

PHYLUM TARDIGRADA	Water bears
PHYLUM PYCNOGONIDA	Sea spiders
PHYLUM ARTHROPODA	Arthropods

PHYLUM TARDIGRADA

Water bears; about 180 species
These small, usually microscopic animals are found in fresh waters and on the seashore. They have flattened bodies and four pairs of short legs. They move clumsily and mostly feed by sucking the sap from plant cells. Example:
Macrobiotus hufelandi: a widespread species in the Northern Hemisphere, living in small pockets of fresh water among mosses and similar habitats

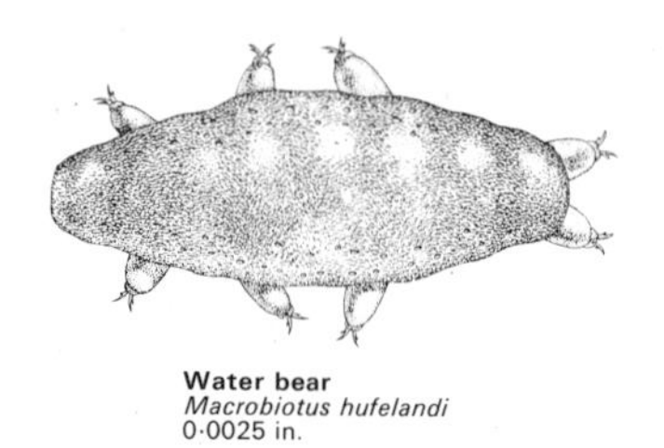

Water bear
Macrobiotus hufelandi
0·0025 in.

PHYLUM PYCNOGONIDA

Sea spiders; about 500 species
This is a small group of marine animals with long narrow bodies and four to seven pairs of legs. The head and thorax are joined and have five segments, and the abdomen is minute. They have no respiratory or excretory organs. Sea spiders are found in all oceans. Example:
Nymphon hirsites: found among algae low in the intertidal zone

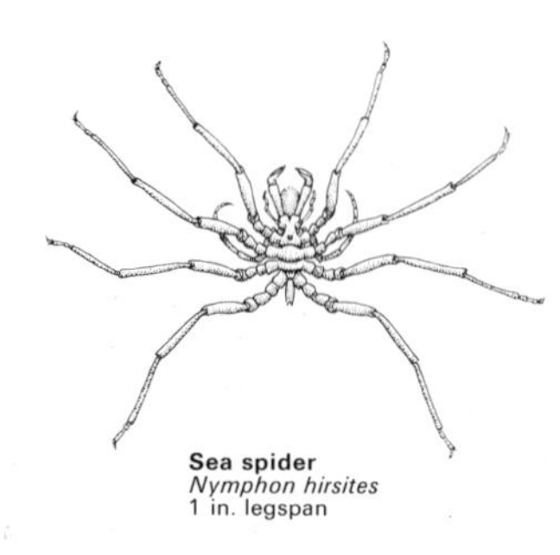

Sea spider
Nymphon hirsites
1 in. legspan

PHYLUM ARTHROPODA

Arthropods
The arthropods form the largest phylum in the animal kingdom. Their bodies, divided into a series of similar segments (like those of annelids, or segmented worms), are encased in a horny layer, or cuticle, which may be flexible, stiff or rigid, and forms an outer skeleton. Some of the body segments bear appendages such as legs or wings, and there is a head or head-like structure bearing sense organs and paired mouth-parts. In the earliest arthropods all the body segments carried appendages. There are 13 classes:

CLASS CRUSTACEA

Crustaceans
Crustaceans, which are primarily aquatic and breathe through gills, have two pairs of antennae, and a body divided into head, thorax and abdomen, although the head and thorax are usually fused. The head part bears three pairs of feeding appendages or mouth-parts. The appendages of crustaceans are usually two-branched. Many crustaceans have oval, unsegmented larvae known as nauplius larvae, with three pairs of appendages. There are eight sub-classes:

SUB-CLASS CEPHALOCARIDA

Cephalocarids; 4 species
These tiny primitive crustaceans were not discovered until 1955. They are shrimp-like, with two-branched appendages on the thorax and abdomen. Example:
Hutchinsoniella macracantha: lives in soft marine sediments and feeds on organic debris. It is found from the intertidal zone to depths of 1000 ft

SUB-CLASS BRANCHIOPODA

Branchiopods; about 1200 species
Branchiopods have flattened, gill-carrying appendages on the trunk; these give them their name—branchiopod means 'gill-foot'. Example:
Brine shrimp *Artemia salina*: found in salty lakes and pools

SUB-CLASS OSTRACODA

Mussel shrimps; 20,000 species
These minute crustaceans range in length from microscopic to over 1 in. The carapace forms two valves which completely enclose the body, like a shellfish. They have only one or two pairs of appendages on their trunks. Example:
Macrocypridina castanea: a fairly widespread marine species

SUB-CLASS COPEPODA

Copepods; 4500 species
This large group of tiny animals—they are only 0·04 in. to $\frac{1}{5}$ in. long—forms an important part of the plankton community of the oceans. Example:
Calanus finmarchicus: lives in northern seas; eaten by herrings

SUB-CLASS MYSTACOCARIDA

Mystacocarids; 3 species
This is a little-known group with only one genus, related to the copepods. Example:
Derocheilocaris ramanei: lives between grains of sand

SUB-CLASS BRANCHIURA

Fish lice; 75 species
All fish lice are parasites, living mainly on the skin and in the gill cavities of fish. They have flattened bodies, sucking mouth-parts and no gills. Example:
Argulus trilineatus: has strong claws and swims strongly with four pairs of swimming legs

SUB-CLASS CIRRIPEDIA

Barnacles; 800 species
Most adult barnacles attach themselves by the head, sometimes with long stalks, to rocks, driftwood and marine animals. Chalky plates usually protect the body. Barnacles feed by protruding the legs through the plates and using them to filter plankton from the water and pass it to the mouth. Example:
Balanus tintinnabulum: found mainly in tropical waters, often attached to the bottoms of boats

SUB-CLASS MALACOSTRACA

Shrimps, prawns, lobsters, crabs and woodlice; about 18,000 species
Crustaceans of this large group are found in many habitats and are very varied in appearance. The body is usually divided into a trunk composed of eight segments and an abdomen of six, each segment bearing appendages. Some species are only 0·02 in. long, while the Japanese spider crab *Macrocheira kaempferi* has an 11 ft limb span and is the largest living arthropod. Examples:
Pill woodlouse *Armadillidium vulgare* (up to $\frac{2}{3}$ in.): common around human habitation. Its back has a smooth, hard surface and it can contract into a ball if danger threatens
Freshwater shrimp *Gammarus lacustris* ($\frac{1}{3}$ in.): found in rivers and lakes and on the seashore. It has seven pairs of walking legs and the female carries her young in a brood pouch between her legs
European lobster *Homarus vulgaris*: lives in shallows round rocky shores

CLASS MEROSTOMATA

King crabs or horseshoe crabs; 5 species
This group, more common in Paleozoic times 570–225 million years ago, is today found mainly in warm seas. These crabs have bodies divided into two sections, both encased in heavy protective plates. The head/thorax carries five pairs of walking legs and a pair of pincers. The other section, the abdomen, terminates in a long spine. The king crab breathes through book-gills on the abdomen, which resemble thin plates arranged like the leaves of a book. Example:
King crab *Limulus polyphemus*: lives on the muddy sea bottom and sandbanks of the north-western Atlantic coast and the Gulf of Mexico

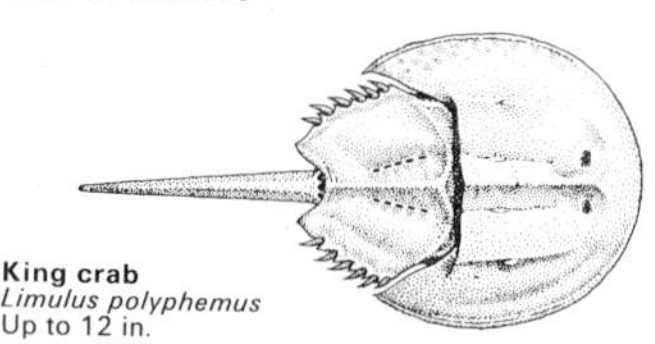

King crab
Limulus polyphemus
Up to 12 in.

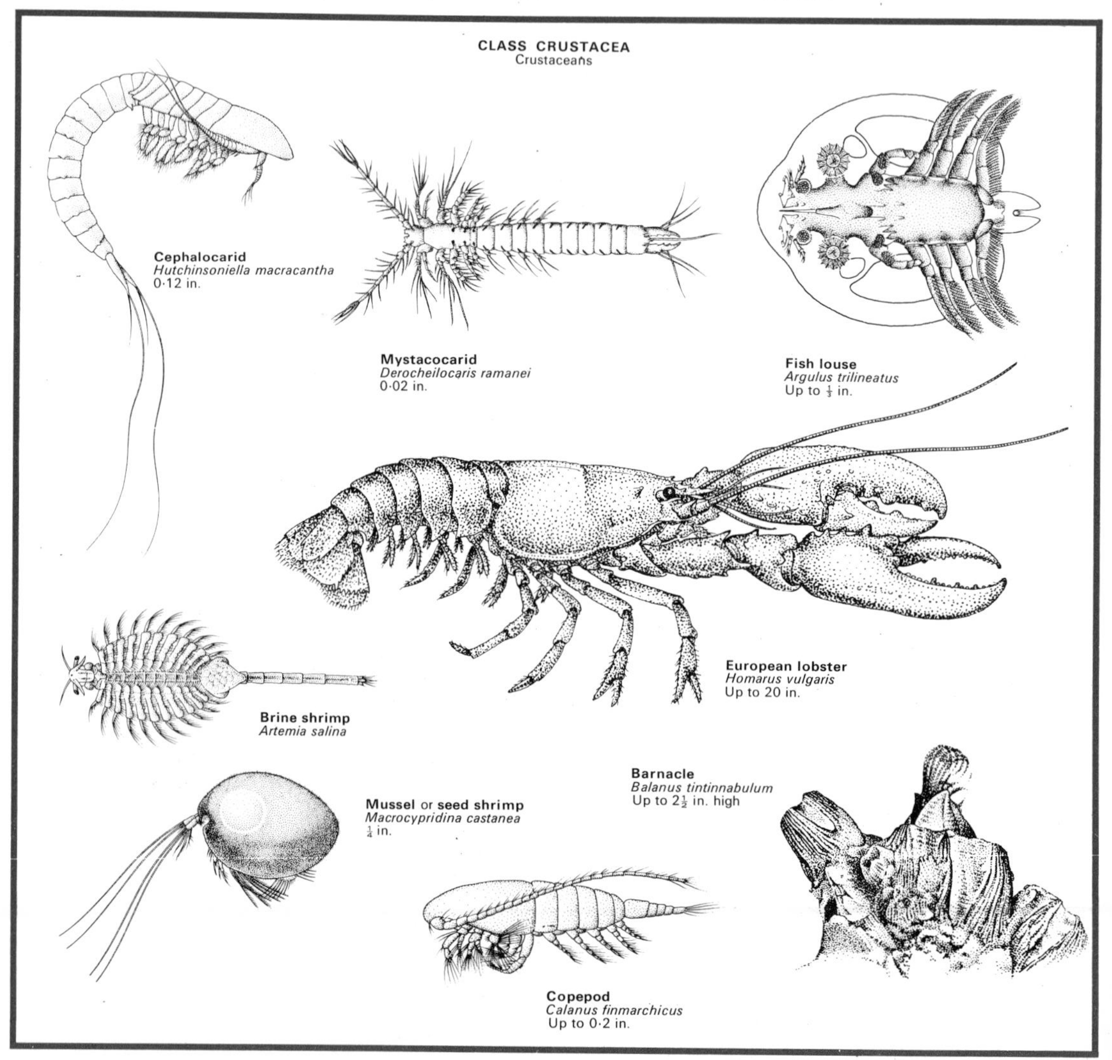

CLASS CRUSTACEA
Crustaceans

Cephalocarid
Hutchinsoniella macracantha
0·12 in.

Mystacocarid
Derocheilocaris ramanei
0·02 in.

Fish louse
Argulus trilineatus
Up to $\frac{1}{3}$ in.

European lobster
Homarus vulgaris
Up to 20 in.

Brine shrimp
Artemia salina

Mussel or **seed shrimp**
Macrocypridina castanea
$\frac{1}{4}$ in.

Barnacle
Balanus tintinnabulum
Up to $2\frac{1}{2}$ in. high

Copepod
Calanus finmarchicus
Up to 0·2 in.

CLASS ARACHNIDA
Arachnids
These are almost all land animals which normally breathe through gill-like structures called book-lungs. Their bodies are divided into two main parts. The first part is the prosoma, bearing two pairs of appendages (the chelicerae and the pedipalps) which are often pincer-like, and four pairs of legs; the second part is an abdomen which lacks limbs. Arachnids are generally aggressive, predatory creatures, preying on small arthropods. There are ten orders:

ORDER SCORPIONIDA
Scorpions; 600 species
These secretive, nocturnal animals are abundant in tropical regions. Their pedipalps are large pincers, but their chelicerae are small. The scorpion's body, which may be $\frac{1}{2}$–7 in. long, has a sting on its last segment. Example:
***Androctonus aeneas*:** found mainly in North Africa, under stones and logs and in burrows. Its venom, produced in two glands at the base of the sting, causes paralysis of the heart and respiratory muscles in mammals

ORDER PSEUDOSCORPIONIDA
Pseudoscorpions; 1100 species
Found throughout the world, these small arachnids live in leaf litter and damp nooks and crannies. They lack stings but have two pairs of pincers: large pedipalps bearing poison glands and small chelicerae containing silk glands. Example:
***Chelifer cancroides*:** found in houses all over the world

ORDER SOLIFUGAE
Camel spiders or sun spiders; 570 species
These large, swift-moving, tropical and sub-tropical animals prefer arid environments. They have large, pincer-like chelicerae and leg-like pedipalps with sensitive adhesive organs. Example:
***Galeodes arabs*:** lives in North Africa, hiding under stones and in crevices

ORDER PALPIGRADI
Micro-whip scorpions; 21 species
These tiny, soil-dwelling arachnids are found in the warmer parts of the world. They have a pair of well-developed pincer-like chelicerae and leg-like pedipalps. The trunk is segmented and ends in a long flagellum, or tail. Example:
***Koenenia mirabilis*:** lives in the Mediterranean region

ORDER UROPYGI
Whip scorpions; 105 species
These small to medium-sized arachnids are named after the very long, narrow, bristle-like structure borne by the last segment of the abdomen. The chelicerae are large and hooked, the pedipalps are short, stout and often pincer-like, and the first pair of legs is very long. Example:
***Mastigoproctus giganteus*:** found in the southern U.S.A. Hides under leaves, rocks and debris during the day

ORDER AMBLYPYGI
Amblypygids; 50 species
These medium-sized arachnids, ranging in length from 0·16 in. to $1\frac{3}{4}$ in., are found in warm countries, usually in damp, dark habitats. The chelicerae and pedipalps are similar to those of whip scorpions, and the first pair of legs, which are long and thin, is held out in front like antennae Example:
***Charinus milloti*:** found in Africa in dark, damp habitats

ORDER ARANEAE
Spiders; 20,000 species
After mites and ticks, spiders are the most widespread and abundant arachnids. Spiders, which range in length from less than 0·03 in. to 10 in., have chelicerae bearing poisonous fangs and have silk glands in the abdomen. The pedipalps, leg-like in the female, are modified into copulatory organs in the male. Many species have excellent vision. Example:
Garden spider *Araneus diadematus*: one of the most common species in Europe. The male is smaller than the female, and is often eaten by her after mating

ORDER RICINULEI
Ricinuleids; about 15 species
These small, compact, little-known arachnids, from Africa and the warmer parts of America, live in leaf mould. Both the chelicerae and the pedipalps are small and pincer-like. Example:
***Ricinoides afzeli*:** lives in Africa

ORDER OPILIONES
Harvestmen or daddy long-legs; 2400 species
Long legs and short compact bodies distinguish these arachnids, which are normally found in moist environments. Their chelicerae are small with pincers, and their pedipalps are leg-like. They are called harvestmen in Britain and daddy long-legs in North America. Example:
***Phalangium opilio*:** one of the most common European species, it is active by night

ORDER ACARINA
Mites and ticks; 10,000 species
Most of this abundant and widespread group of animals are tiny. Many are parasites, and most of the free-living species inhabit leaf-litter. They are arachnids with a false head, or capitulum, set apart from the rest of the body, and carrying mouth-parts. External segmentation is reduced or absent. Larval stages normally have three pairs of legs; nymphal and adult stages four pairs. The chelicerae and pedipalps are pincer-like, leg-like or needle-like, depending on their function. Example:
Harvest mite *Trombicula autumnalis*: common in Europe

CLASS ARACHNIDA
Arachnids

Camel spider
Galeodes arabs
Body up to 3 in.

Amblypygid
Charinus milloti
About $\frac{1}{2}$ in.

Scorpion
Androctonus aeneas
$3\frac{1}{2}$ in.

Harvestman
Phalangium opilio
Body $\frac{1}{8}$ in.

Garden spider
Araneus diadematus
Body about $\frac{1}{2}$ in.

Pseudoscorpion
Chelifer cancroides
Less than $\frac{1}{2}$ in.

Micro-whip scorpion
Koenenia mirabilis
Less than 0·08 in.

Harvest mite
Trombicula autumnalis
Up to 0·04 in.

Whip scorpion
Mastigoproctus giganteus
$2\frac{1}{2}$ in.

Ricinuleid
Ricinoides afzeli
About $\frac{1}{4}$ in.

CLASS ONYCHOPHORA
Velvet worms; about 120 species
These animals live under logs and stones in the tropics and southern temperate regions. They have a soft outer covering, a pair of short legs on each trunk segment and a pair of long antennae. They range from $\frac{1}{2}$ in. to 6 in. in length. Example:
***Peripatopsis capensis*:** lives in South Africa

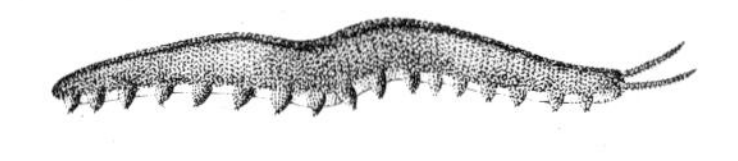

Velvet worm
Peripatopsis capensis
2 in.

CLASS PAUROPODA
Pauropods; 60 species
These tiny arthropods—they are 0·02–0·08 in. long—have a 12-segment body with two pairs of mouth-parts, branched antennae and nine or ten pairs of legs. The plates on the back are alternately large and small. Example:
***Pauropus silvaticus*:** lives in forest humus and soil in north-western Europe

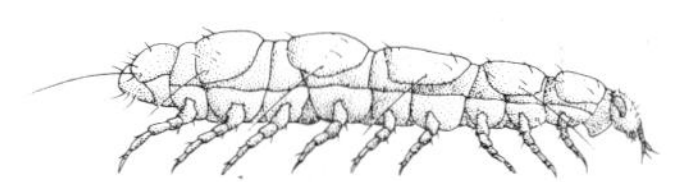

Pauropod
Pauropus silvaticus
0·04 in.

CLASS DIPLOPODA
Millipedes; 8000 species
The millipede's horny outer layer forms a hard armour which is used in head-on burrowing. There are two pairs of mouth-parts, and simple seven-segment antennae. The body segments are cylindrical and joined together in pairs, each bearing two pairs of legs. The longest millipede has no more than 200 legs. Millipedes are usually vegetarian, and are found all over the world. Example:
***Cylindroiulus londinensis*:** a typical burrowing species, which sometimes eats the sprouts of seed grain. The females construct a nest for their eggs. Found in the Northern Hemisphere

Millipede
Cylindroiulus londinensis
$1\frac{1}{2}$ in.

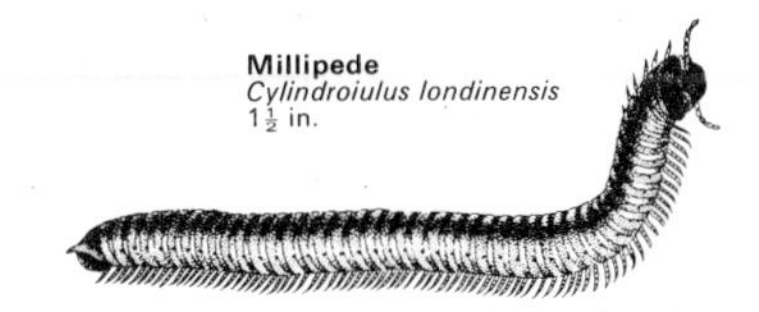

Invertebrates

CLASS CHILOPODA

Centipedes; 2000 species

Centipedes are carnivorous, land-dwelling animals ranging in length from ⅕ in. to 12 in. They have 15–177 pairs of legs, one on each segment. The first pair of legs is modified into poison fangs, and there are three pairs of mouth-parts. Example:
Scolopendra morsitans**:** found mainly in the tropics

Centipede
Scolopendra morsitans
6–8 in.

CLASS SYMPHYLA

Symphylans; 120 species

These small animals—the longest does not exceed ⅓ in.—have a trunk of 14 segments protected by overlapping dorsal plates. The head bears a pair of long segmented antennae and three pairs of mouth-parts. Example:
Scutigerella immaculata**:** found in most parts of the world, under stones, logs and in leaf litter. It causes damage to vegetable and fruit crops

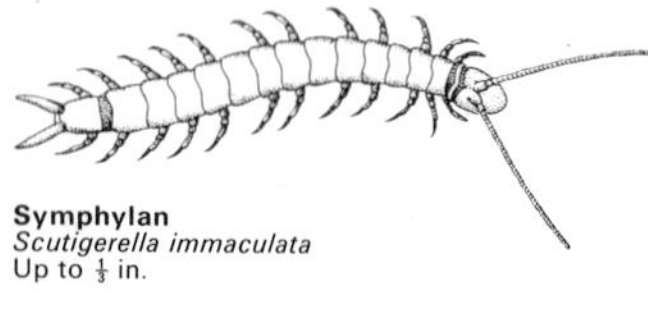

Symphylan
Scutigerella immaculata
Up to ⅓ in.

CLASS COLLEMBOLA

Springtails; 1100 species

Like all the succeeding groups of arthropods, springtails have three pairs of mouth-parts and one pair of antennae on the head, a three-segmented thorax with three pairs of legs, and an abdomen, usually lacking legs. Springtails have six abdominal segments. A forked organ on the end of the abdomen enables the springtail to spring upwards when the fork is suddenly released. They are important animals of the leaf litter, and up to 250 million may live in 1 acre of meadow. Example:
Sminthuroides aquaticus**:** common all over the world in soil or decaying matter. It feeds mainly on fungi, spores and grains of pollen

Springtail
Sminthuroides aquaticus
0·1–0·3 in.

CLASS DIPLURA

Two-pronged bristletails; 400 species

Bristletails have a ten-segmented abdomen, at the end of which are two filaments. They live under stones or logs, or in buried decaying leaves. Example:
Campodea folsomi **:** widely distributed in more northerly regions

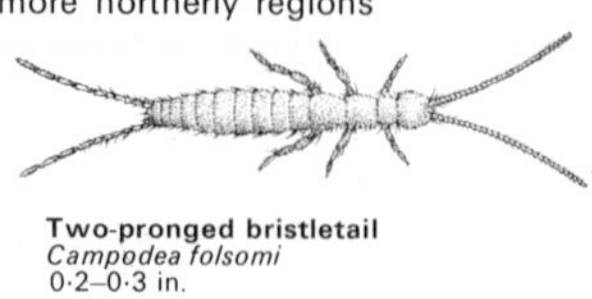

Two-pronged bristletail
Campodea folsomi
0·2–0·3 in.

CLASS PROTURA

Proturans; 45 species

These tiny creatures have a 12-segmented abdomen with tiny appendages on the first three segments. They use their forelegs as feelers, holding them in front of their heads. Example:
Acerentomon doderoi**:** found in Europe in woodland litter

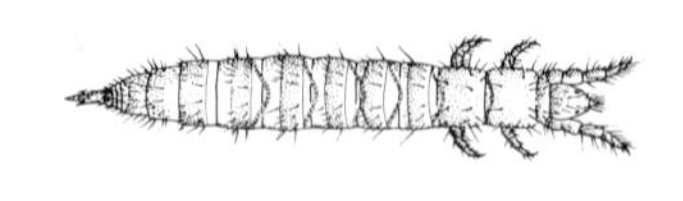

Proturan
Acerentomon doderoi
0·1 in.

CLASS THYSANURA

Three-pronged bristletails; 350 species

The Thysanura have smooth, tapering bodies with long antennae and three long, slender filaments on the abdomen. As they grow, they cast off the outer skeleton which is replaced by a larger one underneath. This occurs throughout life in Thysanura, unlike most arthropods, whose outer skeleton is not shed once maturity is reached. Example:
Silverfish *Lepisma saccharina*: prefers damp, cool situations and is often found in kitchens and bathrooms throughout Europe

Silverfish
Lepisma saccharina
½ in.

CLASS INSECTA

Insects

Insects have a head with one pair of antennae and three pairs of mouth-parts; a three-segmented thorax with a pair of legs on each segment and usually a pair of wings on each of the two rear segments; and a legless abdomen of 11 segments. There are 29 orders:

ORDER EPHEMEROPTERA

Mayflies; 1300 species

Mayflies are fragile insects, usually with four membranous wings, held vertically over the body when at rest; the hind wings are small and may be absent. The aquatic larval stage with gills may last three years before the first adult stage is reached. Then, after a few hours, the skin is shed and the fully functional adult with stronger wings and more lustrous colour appears—only to die after one day. Example:
Ephemera danica**:** always found near water. It is the largest British mayfly

ORDER ODONATA

Dragonflies and damselflies; 4500 species

The members of this order are strong fliers with a long narrow abdomen, very short antennae, huge eyes and legs set well forward to catch the smaller insects they prey on. The well-developed lower lip of the aquatic larva covers the face like a mask, and can be unfolded rapidly to seize small aquatic animals. There are two main sub-orders—the Anisoptera, the dragonflies, which rest with their wings spread out; and the Zygoptera, the more delicate damselflies, which rest with their wings folded back. Example:
Hawker dragonfly *Aeschna juncea*: found in North America, Europe and Asia as far south as Kashmir

ORDER NOTOPTERA

Notopterans; 6 species

These wingless insects, living in the cold mountains of North America, Japan and Siberia, show a combination of features found in other orders. The insects with which they share characteristics include crickets and earwigs. Example:
Grylloblatta campodeiformis **:** found at high latitudes under stones and debris. It was the first known species of this order, and was discovered in 1914 in North America

ORDER PLECOPTERA

Stoneflies; 1300 species

The weak-flying stoneflies, like the mayflies and dragonflies, have aquatic larvae. They are soft-bodied, rather flat insects with a broad head, long antennae and clear wings. Example:
Isoperla confusa**:** found in North America

ORDER EMBIOPTERA

Web-spinners; 150 species

These fragile insects live in silken tunnels under stones, especially in the tropics. The first segments of the forelimbs are expanded and carry silk glands. The female is wingless. Example:
Embia major **:** found in northern India

ORDER BLATTARIA

Cockroaches; 3500 species

Cockroaches have long antennae, short cigar-shaped bodies, and thick leathery forewings which protect the hind wings. When at rest, the wings are folded back and lie on the abdomen. Example:
Oriental cockroach *Blatta orientalis*: a domestic species found all over the world. It is dark brown, with small wings and is sometimes called the black beetle

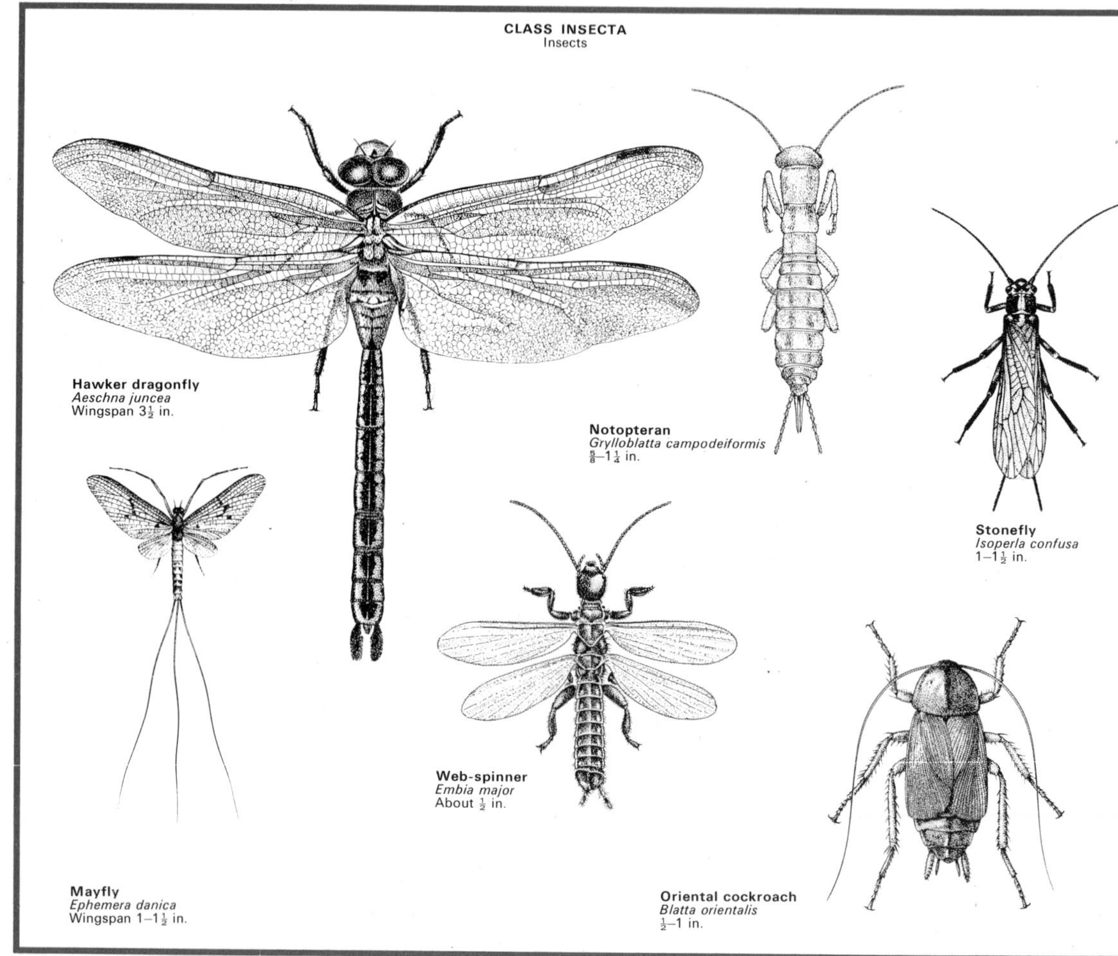

ORDER MANTODEA

Mantids; 1800 species

These insects sit motionless as if praying, then quickly grasp an insect, impaling it on the sharp spines of their front legs. The female eats the male after mating has taken place. Example:

Praying mantis *Mantis religiosa*: found in western Europe and introduced into eastern America. It is pale green

ORDER ISOPTERA

Termites; 1900 species

Termites are near-relatives of cockroaches but differ from them in having two small pairs of fragile wings which are shed after a brief courtship flight, and before mating. The mated pairs found colonies, which may vary in numbers from a hundred to hundreds of thousands of termites living in large elaborate nests, or in galleries built in wood or soil. Termites have a highly developed social organisation based on many castes. The female, or queen, fertilised at intervals by the king, becomes distended, like a soft white sausage. The workers—small, wingless, sterile offspring—construct the nest, care for the eggs and find food. Sterile and wingless soldiers, often with big heads and jaws, defend the colony. Colonies may last up to 100 years. Example:

Reticulitermes flavipes: a destructive subterranean species found in North America

ORDER ZORAPTERA

Zorapterans; 16 species

These minute insects, less than $\frac{1}{8}$ in. long, are related to the book-lice. They live under bark in decaying wood and in humus in West Africa, Ceylon, Java, Texas, Florida and Bolivia. Example:

Zorotypus guineensis: found in Africa

ORDER ORTHOPTERA

Grasshoppers, crickets and allies; 10,000 species

Most of the Orthoptera have long hind legs with powerful thighs enabling them to make long jumps. They make noises by rubbing hard parts of the body together and they have hearing organs. Leathery forewings protect the fan-like hind wings. Locusts, which swarm in huge numbers and destroy vegetation, are members of this order. Example:

Desert locust *Schistocerca gregaria*: found in northern Africa, Arabia and the Near East, through India to Assam

ORDER PHASMIDA

Stick-insects and leaf-insects; 2000 species

The bodies of these predominantly tropical insects are either thin and twig-like, or flattened like leaves. They remain motionless by day, disguised by their resemblance to plants, and feed and move at night. Their eggs, which are large and hard-shelled, resemble seeds. Example:

Didymuria violescens: lives in Australia, where it defoliates alpine ash

ORDER DERMAPTERA

Earwigs; 900 species

These insects have horny forceps, used in defence. Short leathery forewings protect the delicate semicircular hind wings, which are pleated like a fan. Example:

Common European earwig *Forficula auricularia*: native to Europe and introduced into North and South America, South Africa and Australasia. It is omnivorous and nocturnal

ORDER PSOCOPTERA

Book-lice; 1000 species

These tiny, soft-bodied insects with long antennae are found on trees or under bark and stones. Some are wingless. Example:

Liposcelis divinatorius: found in temperate regions of the Northern Hemisphere. It feeds on fragments of both animal and vegetable matter, including the paste of book bindings

ORDER MALLOPHAGA

Bird-lice; 2600 species

These tiny, wingless, rather flat insects with small eyes live as parasites on birds and some mammals. They feed on feathers and skin, and some drink blood. Example:

Chicken louse *Menacanthus stramineus*: a pest of domestic poultry in all parts of the world

ORDER ANOPLURA

Sucking-lice; 250 species

These parasites on mammals have mouth-parts which are adapted for biting or piercing the skin for blood. Example:

Human louse *Pediculus humanus*: found world wide on man, and responsible for typhus

ORDER THYSANOPTERA

Thrips; 5000 species

These small, slender-bodied insects, common on flower-heads, especially dandelions, have piercing mouth-parts and tiny narrow wings fringed with hairs. Example:

Red-banded thrips *Heliothrips rubrocinctus*: widespread in North America. It sucks plant juices and may transmit plant viruses

ORDER HEMIPTERA

Bugs; 55,000 species

All the members of this diverse order have mouth-parts in the form of a beak, with the jaws transformed into thread-like stylets capable of piercing and sucking. The forewings have a thickened membranous section which overlaps the abdomen when the wings are at rest. The sub-order Heteroptera includes bed-bugs, waterboatmen and water scorpions. The sub-order Homoptera includes cicadas and aphids. Example:

Apple aphid *Aphis pomi*: occurs on plants and trees in the Northern Hemisphere. It attacks leaves, shoots and blossoms

ORDER NEUROPTERA

Lacewings and ant-lions; 4000 species

These insects, which vary greatly in size, are usually predatory. The adults have biting mouth-parts and gauzy, net-like wings which form a roof over the abdomen when at rest. Their larvae are predatory. Example:

Green lacewing *Chrysopa flava*: widely distributed in Europe

ORDER MEGALOPTERA

Alderflies; 500 species

These insects are commonly found on vegetation near water. Their larvae are aquatic, with gills on the abdominal segments. Example:

Alderfly *Sialis lutaria*: common in Britain and throughout Europe

ORDER RAPHIDIODEA

Snakeflies; 80 species

This group is found in all continents except Australia. Most species have unusual neck-like extensions of the thorax and the female lays eggs under bark, particularly of conifers, through a long needle-like ovipositor. Example:

Snakefly *Raphidia notata*: found in woods, shrubs and rank vegetation

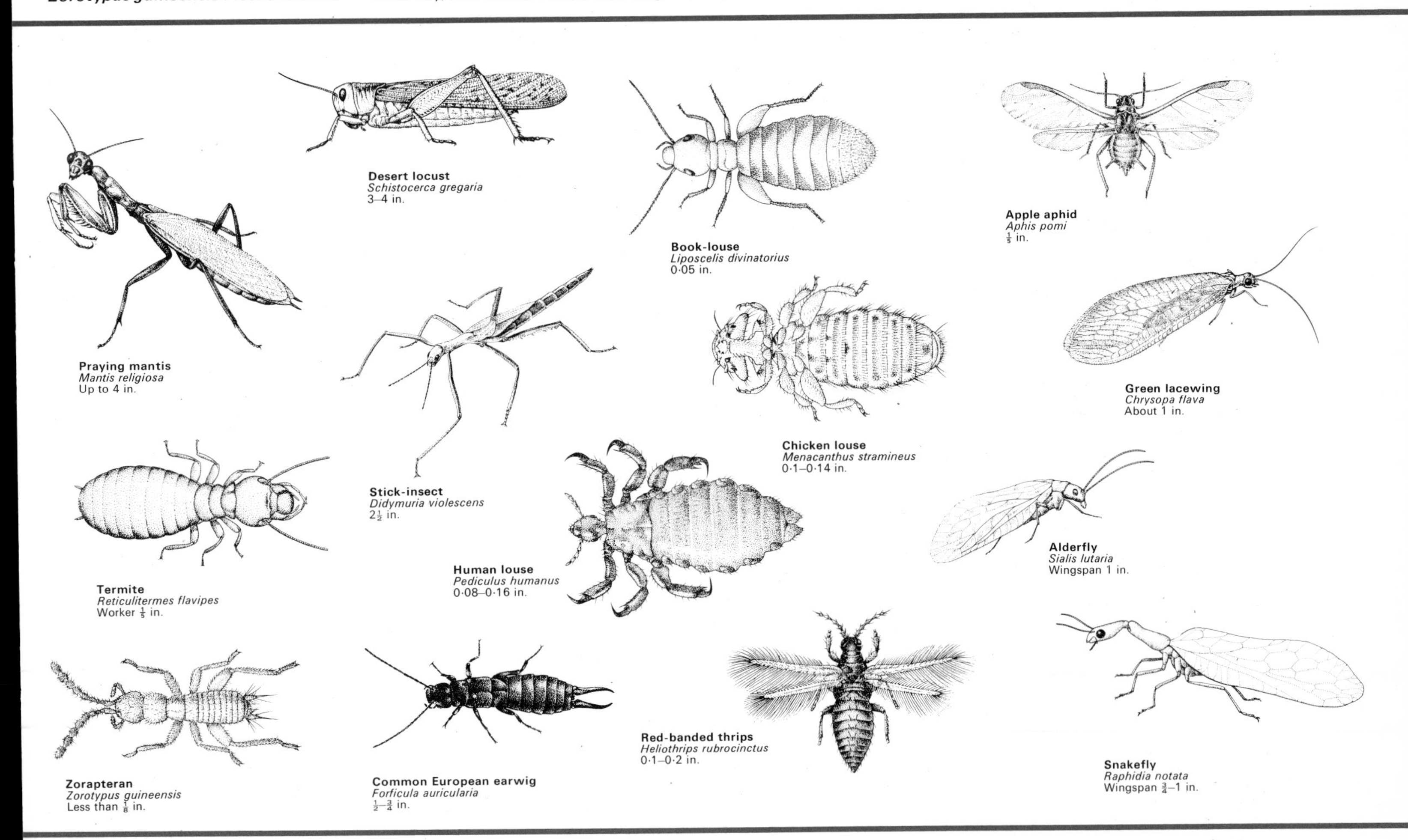

Praying mantis *Mantis religiosa* Up to 4 in.

Desert locust *Schistocerca gregaria* 3–4 in.

Book-louse *Liposcelis divinatorius* 0·05 in.

Apple aphid *Aphis pomi* $\frac{1}{8}$ in.

Green lacewing *Chrysopa flava* About 1 in.

Stick-insect *Didymuria violescens* $2\frac{1}{2}$ in.

Chicken louse *Menacanthus stramineus* 0·1–0·14 in.

Termite *Reticulitermes flavipes* Worker $\frac{1}{3}$ in.

Human louse *Pediculus humanus* 0·08–0·16 in.

Alderfly *Sialis lutaria* Wingspan 1 in.

Zorapteran *Zorotypus guineensis* Less than $\frac{1}{8}$ in.

Common European earwig *Forficula auricularia* $\frac{1}{2}$–$\frac{3}{4}$ in.

Red-banded thrips *Heliothrips rubrocinctus* 0·1–0·2 in.

Snakefly *Raphidia notata* Wingspan $\frac{3}{4}$–1 in.

Invertebrates

PHYLUM ARTHROPODA	Arthropods
PHYLUM CHAETOGNATHA	Arrow worms
PHYLUM POGONOPHORA	Beard-bearers
PHYLUM ECHINODERMATA	Echinoderms

ORDER COLEOPTERA
Beetles; 300,000 species

About 30–40 per cent of all insects are beetles. They vary greatly in size and structure, but can be easily recognised because their forewings are modified into horny sheaths completely concealing the hind wings when the insect is not flying. Their sizes range from 0·03 in. to 6 in. long, and the heavily built Goliath beetle *Goliathus giganteus* is 8 million times heavier than the smallest species. Beetles live in water or on land, and some burrow in the soil. Their larvae vary from legless grubs to caterpillar-like forms preying on other insects. Example:

Common dor beetle *Geotrupes stercorarius*: found in burrows under cattle or horse dung throughout Europe and northern Asia

ORDER STREPSIPTERA
Strepsipterans; 300 species

The larvae of these insects are parasites in bugs, ants, bees and wasps. The adult female, which is little more than a sac of eggs, never leaves the host. The male is winged and free-living, but has only hind wings, the forewings being represented by balancing organs which are important in regulating stable flight. Example:

Stylops shannoni found in North America, where it is parasitic on solitary species of bees

ORDER MECOPTERA
Scorpionflies; 300 species

The elongated heads of these insects point vertically downwards. The male has prominent reproductive organs contained in the last segment of the abdomen, which curl up over the back like a scorpion's tail. Example:

Common scorpionfly *Panorpa communis*: inhabits sunny hedgerows in Europe, from Britain to Scandinavia. It feeds mainly on dead or dying insects

ORDER TRICHOPTERA
Caddisflies; 3500 species

These weak-flying flies are moth-like in appearance, but their wings are hairy, not scaly. Their mouth-parts are adapted for licking fluids but probably many do not feed at all as adults. The aquatic larvae, sometimes called caddis worms, build and live in protective cases made of secreted silk, stones, leaves or shells. Example:

Rhyacophila fenestra: found in North America

ORDER ZEUGLOPTERA
Zeuglopterans; 100 species

These small moth-like insects are found in large numbers on flowers such as buttercups in spring. They feed on pollen. Example:

Micropterix calthella: common throughout Europe

ORDER LEPIDOPTERA
Butterflies and moths; 120,000 species

Six of the 80 families of this large group consist of brightly coloured, day-active butterflies, most of which fold their wings vertically; the rest are moths, which fold their wings horizontally and are mostly nocturnal. All members of the order have two pairs of wings covered with powdery scales and a long sucking proboscis formed from one pair of mouth-parts. This is coiled when not in use. Example:

Peacock butterfly *Nymphalis io*: found in Europe, and from northern Asia to Japan. It passes the winter in adult form, sleeping in hollow trees, and emerges in early spring to breed

ORDER DIPTERA
True flies; 75,000 species

The true flies have only one pair of functional wings, the hind pair being reduced to a pair of knobs used to maintain balance. One group includes the slender-bodied midges, craneflies (known as daddy long-legs in Britain) and mosquitoes. Another contains the blood-sucking horse-flies and clegs, and a third, the compactly built houseflies, bluebottles, hoverflies and fruit flies with mouths adapted for sucking fluids. The soft, plump-bodied larvae, called maggots, usually feed on decaying matter or dung. Example:

Housefly *Musca domestica*: found wherever man lives. The larvae develop in rotten plant or animal matter and adults transmit diseases

ORDER SIPHONAPTERA
Fleas; 1800 species

Adult fleas are parasites on birds and mammals. They are brown, wingless insects with bristly, vertically compressed bodies. The mouth-parts are modified for piercing and sucking, and in many species the well-developed hind legs are used for jumping. Example:

Common rat flea *Nosopsyllus fasciatus*: widely distributed, particularly in the Northern Hemisphere. It feeds on man as well as on its rodent hosts

ORDER HYMENOPTERA
Ants, bees and wasps; 100,000 species

Members of this group have two pairs of glossy, membranous wings, and the forewings are linked to the hind wings. The mouth-parts are primarily adapted for biting, and often for lapping and sucking as well. There are two sub-orders. The Symphyta includes the saw-flies and the wood wasps, which insert their eggs into plants and have no obvious 'wasp waist' between the thorax and the abdomen. The Apocrita includes the parasitic gall wasps, which lay their eggs in plants; ichneumon flies, which lay their eggs in the larvae or eggs of other insects; and the free-living bees, wasps and ants, which have a noticeable waist and seek food for their larvae. Many of these live in complex societies. Example:

Honey bee *Apis mellifera*: common in northern Europe. It nests in the wild in caves or hollow trees, or more often in artificially housed colonies, with a queen and a number of males (drones), which are fed by the workers (sterile females). Workers are slightly smaller than drones

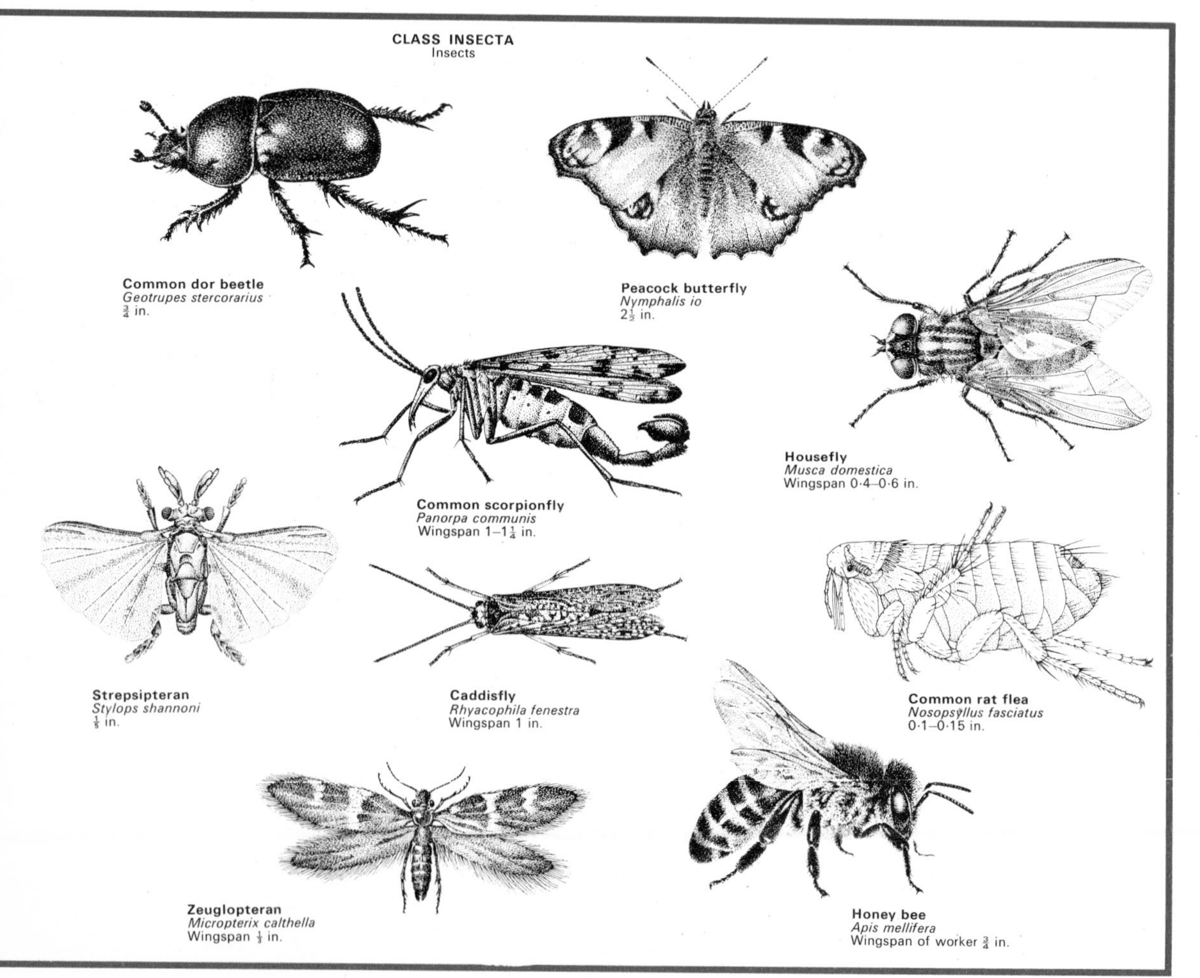

CLASS INSECTA
Insects

Common dor beetle
Geotrupes stercorarius
¾ in.

Peacock butterfly
Nymphalis io
2½ in.

Housefly
Musca domestica
Wingspan 0·4–0·6 in.

Common scorpionfly
Panorpa communis
Wingspan 1–1¼ in.

Strepsipteran
Stylops shannoni
⅕ in.

Caddisfly
Rhyacophila fenestra
Wingspan 1 in.

Common rat flea
Nosopsyllus fasciatus
0·1–0·15 in.

Zeuglopteran
Micropterix calthella
Wingspan ⅓ in.

Honey bee
Apis mellifera
Wingspan of worker ¾ in.

PHYLUM CHAETOGNATHA
Arrow worms; about 50 species

These worms are abundant in marine plankton and feed on microscopic single-celled plants and small planktonic animals. They have a well-developed body cavity, and the elongated body is divided into a head with eyes and horny teeth, a trunk and a tail. There are fins on the side and tail. One genus is not planktonic, but lives on the sea floor. Most species are tropical. Example:

Sagitta elegans: inhabits coastal North Atlantic waters

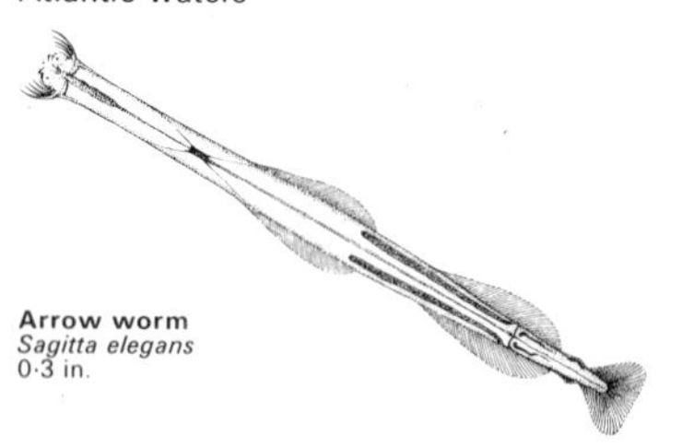

Arrow worm
Sagitta elegans
0·3 in.

PHYLUM POGONOPHORA
Beard-bearers; 80 species

These small, tube-dwelling animals are found in the sea at depths of 6000–30,000 ft, and are related to the annelid worms *Phylum annelida*. Their bodies are in three parts; the proboscis bearing the tentacles, the main body, and a segmented and bristly region. They have a well-developed blood system, but no gut. The food is most probably trapped inside the animals' tentacles and digested there. The sexes are separate, although externally males and females look alike. The first specimen ever found was dredged from Indonesian waters in 1900. Example:

Spirobrachia grandis: this species has more tentacles than average

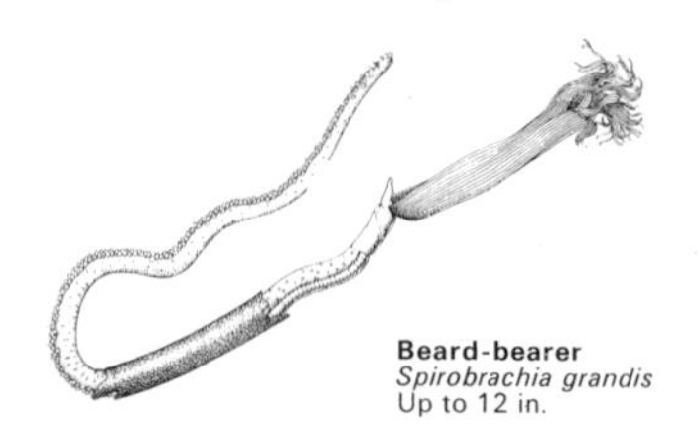

Beard-bearer
Spirobrachia grandis
Up to 12 in.

PHYLUM ECHINODERMATA
Echinoderms

Of the higher invertebrates with a body cavity, only echinoderms are symmetrically radial in form. Most echinoderms can move, though slowly. They have no head and no true brain for overall co-ordination of the body. Externally, they are covered by chalky plates just under the skin and, sometimes, by spines. The mouth is usually on the lower surface of the body. There are five classes:

PHYLUM ECHINODERMATA	Echinoderms
PHYLUM HEMICHORDATA	Hemichordates
PHYLUM CHORDATA	Chordates
SUB-PHYLUM TUNICATA	Tunicates
SUB-PHYLUM CEPHALO-CHORDATA	Lancelets

CLASS ASTEROIDEA

Starfish; 1600 species

Most starfish have five arms radiating from a central disc, though some have as many as 40. They move by means of very small tube-feet bearing suckers which run down the underside of each arm; they have chalky plates buried in the skin, though these do not form a shell. Starfish are usually carnivorous; some feed on small organisms swallowed whole, others on microscopic morsels conveyed to the mouth by cilia. They have remarkable powers of regeneration; provided one-fifth of the central disc is attached to an arm, the entire starfish will grow again. The sexes are separate. Example:

Common starfish *Asterias rubens*: often found just below low tide mark on North Atlantic coasts. It feeds on mussels

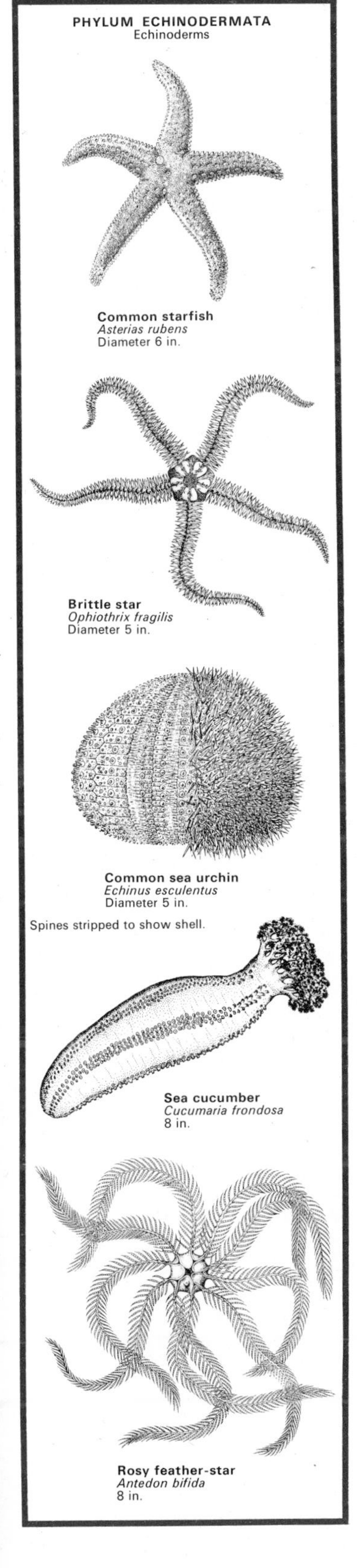

CLASS OPHIUROIDEA

Brittle stars; about 2000 species

The members of this class are star-shaped, with arms which are much more slender than the central disc of the body. They move by means of their arms, and the tube-feet, which play little part in locomotion, lack suckers. Brittle stars feed on plankton and decaying matter. Example:

Ophiothrix fragilis: common off the coasts of north-western Europe

CLASS ECHINOIDEA

Sea urchins; about 800 species

The echinoids, found on the seabed or buried in sand, are circular or oval in shape and do not have arms. The chalky plates in the skin form a complete shell, and the bodies are covered with spines. They feed on both animal and plant matter, and move by means of tube-feet bearing suckers. Example:

Common sea urchin *Echinus esculentus*: common in both the Atlantic and the Mediterranean

CLASS HOLOTHUROIDEA

Sea cucumbers or cotton-spinners; about 900 species

These elongated animals have no arms. Some of the tube-feet near the mouth are adapted as tentacles; the rest have suckers and are used in locomotion. Sea cucumbers feed on decaying matter, swallowed with sand from the seabed, or on small floating organisms. Example:

Cucumaria frondosa: a sea cucumber of the North Atlantic

CLASS CRINOIDEA

Sea-lilies; about 80 species

This is an ancient group and little is known about their way of life. Surviving forms living on the beds of deep seas are permanently attached to a stalk; those in shallower water become detached from the stalk when adult and swim by waving their branched arms. They are the only echinoderms with the mouth on the upper surface of the body. Example:

Rosy feather-star *Antedon bifida*: found on the European continental shelf. It feeds on small particles conveyed to the mouth by ciliary action

PHYLUM HEMICHORDATA

Hemichordates

These marine animals were once classified with the chordates but are now thought to be unrelated. What was thought to be a notochord in them has been shown to be merely an extension of the gut. Their bodies are divided into three regions, the proboscis, collar and trunk, each containing part of the body cavity, or coelom. There are two classes:

CLASS ENTEROPNEUSTA

Acorn worms; 70 species

These worm-shaped animals inhabit sand and mud on the shore and in shallow waters. The sexes are separate. Example:

Atlantic acorn worm *Saccoglossus kowalevskii*: is common in Europe and the Atlantic coast of North America

CLASS PTEROBRANCHIA

Pterobranchs; 20 species

Most of these small animals live on the seabed in tubes secreted by themselves. The collar bears a number of branched arms, carrying cilia which collect planktonic food. Some pterobranchs live in colonies. Example:

Rhabdopleura normani: found near European coasts. It lives in colonies in which the individuals are connected to one another inside a system of tubes

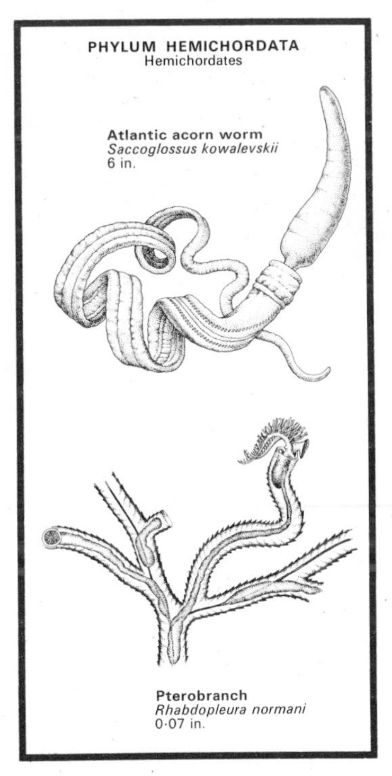

PHYLUM CHORDATA

Chordates

This is a large, varied and highly successful group of complex multi-cellular animals which at some stage in their life history have a supporting skeletal rod or notochord, a hollow dorsal nerve cord, and gills. This phylum includes the vertebrates. It also includes two other sub-phyla of animals which lack backbones, but resemble vertebrates in certain important respects. These are:

SUB-PHYLUM TUNICATA

Tunicates

These unsegmented marine chordates, with no body cavity, are protected by a tough outer tunic usually consisting of a cellulose-type substance called tunicin. The tadpole-like larvae have a notochord in the tail, but the adults, apart from their gills, bear little resemblance to other chordates. They feed by filtering sea water. Enormous quantities are involved: a tunicate an inch or so long may filter 300 pints a day. There are three classes:

CLASS ASCIDIACEA

Sea squirts; 1200 species

Most of these sedentary tunicates live near the seashore, attached to rocks, shells and the bottoms of ships. They range from pea-size to the size of a large potato. Like most tunicates, they are usually hermaphrodites. Some are colonial and reproduce asexually. Example:

Ciona intestinalis: found in European coastal waters

CLASS THALIACEA

Salps; 30 species

Salps are free-floating, sometimes colonial, tunicates, much resembling sea squirts in structure and mode of life. They reproduce sexually, and also asexually, by budding. Most species live in tropical and sub-tropical waters. Example:

Pyrosoma: Salps of this genus live in phosphorescent, cylindrical colonies which vary in length from a few inches to several feet. Some giant colonies recently discovered in Australian waters measure up to 30 ft long

CLASS LARVACEA

Larvaceans; 30 species

These tiny, transparent, free-floating animals feed on tiny planktonic organisms which are caught on filters of a house that the animal builds. Example:

Oikopleura albicans: is common in North Atlantic waters

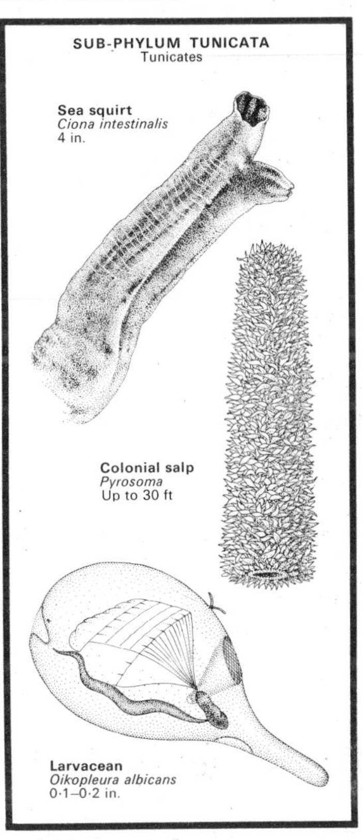

SUB-PHYLUM CEPHALOCHORDATA

Lancelets; 20 species

These are small segmented animals found close to the shore on sandy bottoms. They are the most fish-like of the non-vertebrate chordates and bury themselves in sand, leaving only the head visible. They have a notochord and dorsal nerve cord, and feed on particles taken in at the mouth and filtered through the gill-slits. Reproduction is sexual, and the sexes are separate. Example:

Branchiostoma lanceolatus: found in European coastal waters. It is covered by a transparent, iridescent cuticle. It swims and burrows by rapidly flexing its body, waves of contractions passing through it

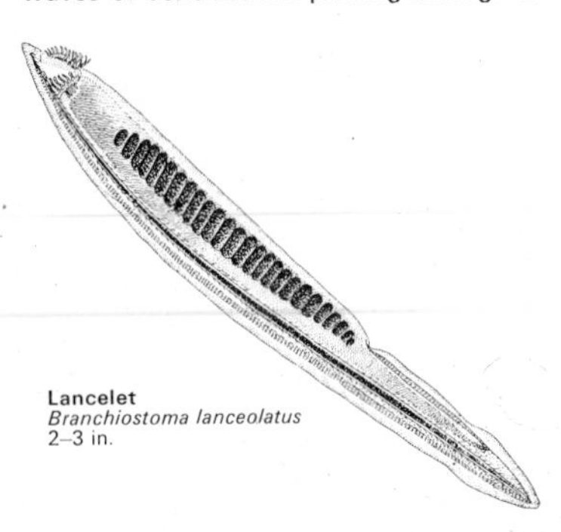

CLASSIFICATION

Fish

PHYLUM CHORDATA	Animals with notochords
SUB-PHYLUM VERTEBRATA	Animals with backbones

All vertebrates are chordates. What distinguishes them from the lower chordates, such as seasquirts and lancelets, is that in vertebrates the notochord, a rod of cells along the back, is strengthened or replaced by a backbone (either of bone or cartilage), and the brain is protected by a cranium

CLASS AGNATHA	Jawless fish
CLASS CHONDRICHTHYES	Cartilaginous fish
CLASS OSTEICHTHYES	Bony fish

CLASS AGNATHA

Jawless fish
The world's first vertebrates belonged to this class; the few living representatives belong to this single order:

ORDER CYCLOSTOMATA
Hagfish and lampreys; 45 species
Lampreys and hagfish are parasites and scavengers. They lack scales and jaws.

Hagfish remain buried in mud, sand or gravel during the day and emerge at night to scavenge on dead animals and organic waste, or to act as parasites on live prey. Their eyes are vestigial and sightless. They hunt by touch and smell; the tip of their snout bears fleshy, sensitive tentacles, called barbels.

Lampreys attach themselves by suckers to the flanks of fish, then rasp through their prey's flesh and drain it of blood. Adult lampreys die after egg-laying and fertilisation; the eggs are laid in the gravel of stream beds and, although some species return to the sea as they mature, others remain in fresh water. Examples:
Glutinous Atlantic hag *Myxine glutinosa* (18 in.): found on both sides of the North Atlantic
Sea lamprey *Petromyzon marinus*: it has a similar range to the glutinous Atlantic hag

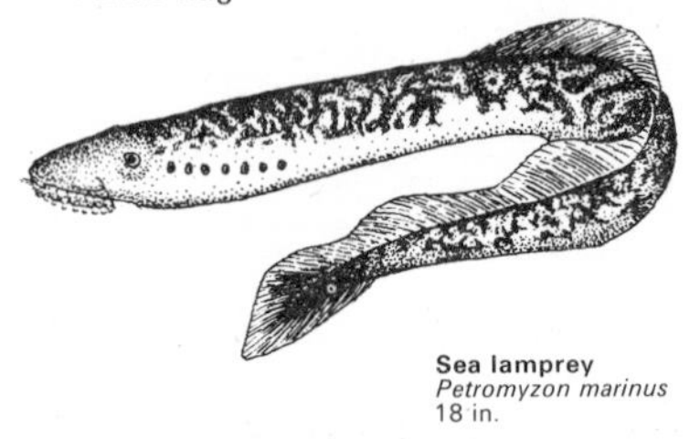
Sea lamprey
Petromyzon marinus
18 in.

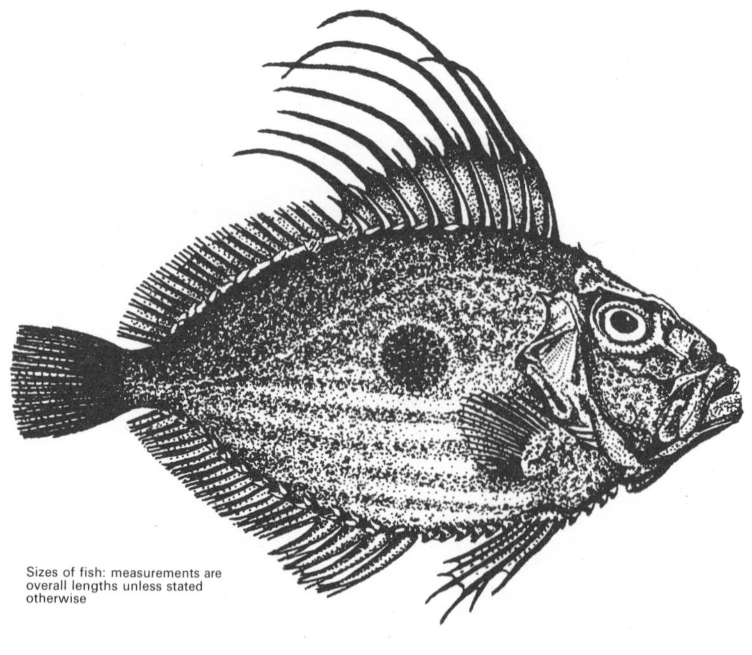
Sizes of fish: measurements are overall lengths unless stated otherwise

Fish, although they all live in water, are cold-blooded, have muscular, streamlined bodies and for the most part breathe through gills, do not form a single natural group. They fall into three classes as distinct from one another as are reptiles from mammals.

CLASS CHONDRICHTHYES

Cartilaginous fish
These jawed fish have skeletons composed primarily of cartilage, with mosaics of small, bony plates as reinforcements.

They have paired stabilising fins and their mouths are adapted for biting, with a band of teeth attached to each jaw. They have small, tooth-like scales, covered with an enamel-like substance. There is no swim-bladder; lift is provided by the flattened head, pectoral fins and tail.

The sense of smell is well developed and the lateral line system, the pressure-sensitive organs with which fish detect vibrations in the sea, is highly developed. The male fertilises the eggs while they are still inside the female, by means of a pair of claspers on the inner edge of the pelvic fins. There are two sub-classes:

SUB-CLASS ELASMOBRANCHII
Sharks and rays
These have five to seven pairs of gills, numerous teeth, and an upper jaw which is not attached to the cranium. They lack swim-bladders. There are two orders:

ORDER SELACHII
Sharks; 200 species
All sharks are good swimmers, with cigar-shaped bodies and gill slits at the side of the head. Most are predators and some are dangerous to man. There are a few freshwater species. Dogfish are merely small sharks, 1–2 ft long. Example:
Basking shark *Cetorhinus maximus*: found in the North Atlantic; it is the second largest living fish—only the whale shark *Rhincodon typus* is larger, growing to 60 ft

ORDER BATOIDEA
Skates and rays; 350 species
Members of this order have flat bodies with wing-like pectoral fins attached to the sides of the head. Examples:
Atlantic manta *Manta birostris* (20 ft wide): moves through surface waters of the temperate and tropical Atlantic with leisurely flaps of its wing-like pectoral fins, scooping in plankton with the horns at the side of its mouth
Common sawfish *Pristis pectinatus* (18 ft): found in tropical and sub-tropical Atlantic waters. The sawfish uses its long, narrow snout with a series of teeth on each side to forage in the mud or to stun fish, slashing its saw from side to side
Thornback ray *Raja clavata*: found in the eastern North Atlantic and the Mediterranean Sea, where it preys upon bottom-living crustaceans

SUB-CLASS HOLOCEPHALI
There is one order:

ORDER CHIMAERIFORMES
Chimaeras; 25 species
These fish have an upper jaw immovably fixed to the cranium, four pairs of gills and six pairs of grinding teeth, which resemble small, flat plates. The males have a clasper in front of the eyes, probably used during courtship, and a pair in front of the pelvic fins. They live near the sea bottom. The spine in front of the dorsal fin is venomous in some species. Example:
Rat fish *Chimaera monstrosa*: found in the eastern Atlantic and the Mediterranean

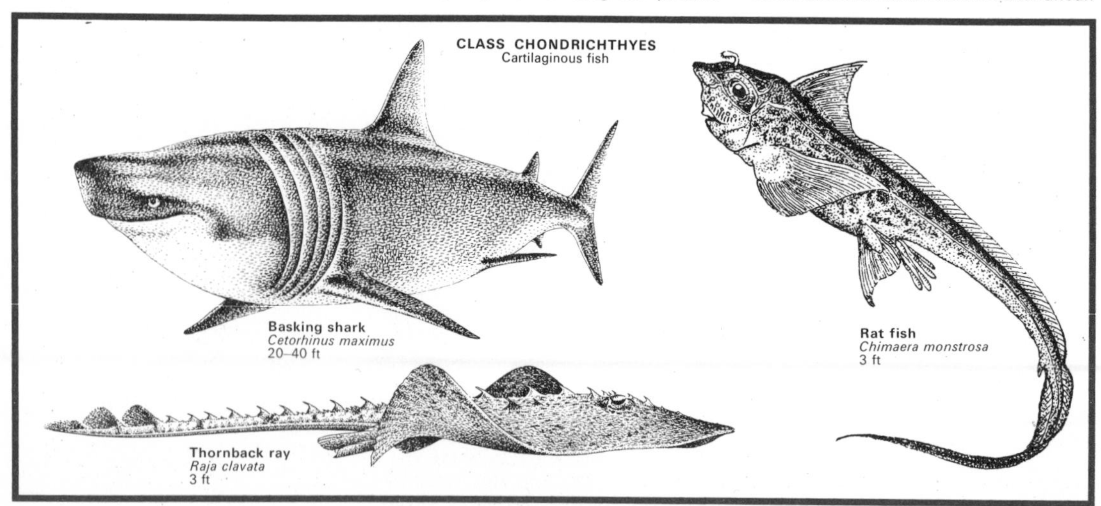
CLASS CHONDRICHTHYES
Cartilaginous fish

Basking shark
Cetorhinus maximus
20–40 ft

Rat fish
Chimaera monstrosa
3 ft

Thornback ray
Raja clavata
3 ft

CLASS OSTEICHTHYES

Bony fish
The bony fish, by far the most numerous of the three classes, have skeletons made of bone. Their teeth are fixed into the upper jaw and they have a lung opening into the gullet which may be converted into a swim-bladder. There are two sub-classes:

SUB-CLASS ACTINOPTERYGII
Ray-finned fish
The fins of these fish are strengthened by bony rays which are jointed. They have large eyes, no internal nostrils, and a lung which is usually converted into a swim-bladder. There are three infra-classes:

INFRA-CLASS CHONDROSTEI
These fish have scales with a thick layer of enamel-like ganoine, and an elongated mouth with the lower jaw hinged far back. There are two orders:

ORDER POLYPTERIFORMES
Bichirs; 12 species
These African fish, with five to 18 flag-like finlets instead of a dorsal fin, have air-breathing lungs. They are found in tropical African rivers and feed on worms, insect larvae and small fish. Example:
Weeks' bichir *Polypterus weeksi*: found in the Congo River. It is protected by rows of scales connected by fibres. It can survive out of water for hours

ORDER ACIPENSERIFORMES
Sturgeons; 22 species
Members of this order are found in temperate or Arctic rivers and coastal waters. Sturgeons have shark-like bodies with scales only along the sides, well-developed swim-bladders and often upturned tails. Examples:
Royal sturgeon *Huso huso* (up to 28 ft): found in the Caspian, Adriatic and Black Seas. This fish weighs about a ton, and caviar is made from its roe
Atlantic sturgeon *Acipenser oxyrhynchus*: found in the Atlantic coastal waters of North America and the Gulf of Mexico. It uses its long snout which bears sensitive barbels to forage through mud and sand for small invertebrates

INFRA-CLASS HOLOSTEI
Like the Chondrostei, from which they developed some 300 million years ago, holostean fish have scales with a layer of ganoine. Unlike them, however, they have jaws that hinge near the front of the head and are not rigidly connected to the skull. There are two orders:

ORDER SEMIONOTIFORMES
Garpikes; 7 species
These fish, which sometimes reach a length of 10 ft, are distinguished by their elongated snouts, air-breathing lungs, and the positions of their dorsal and anal fins, which are far back on the body, directly in front of the tail. They drift along sluggishly, taking their prey with sudden, sideways snaps. Example:
Long-nosed garpike *Lepisosteus osseus*: found in North American fresh waters from the Mississippi basin eastwards; it will imitate driftwood in order to get closer to fish it preys on

ORDER AMIIFORMES
There is one species:
Bowfin *Amia calva*: found in North American rivers and swamps. It has a long, arching, spineless dorsal fin. Males make nests of aquatic plants in which the eggs incubate. They guard the nests and the young fish after they hatch. Bowfins prey on fish and invertebrates

PHYLUM CHORDATA	Animals with notochords
SUB-PHYLUM VERTEBRATA	Animals with backbones
CLASS OSTEICHTHYES	Bony fish

INFRA-CLASS TELEOSTEI

The teleosts are the most numerous group of living vertebrates. They evolved from the holosteans about 190 million years ago, and have no ganoine in their scales. The tail fin is symmetrical, its rays fanning out from enlarged bones at the end of the spines, and the upper jaw is attached to the skull only at the snout. The swim-bladder, which functions almost entirely as a buoyancy control, is lost in many species. These fish tend to be highly vocal and social. There are 30 orders:

ORDER ELOPIFORMES
Tarpons; 12 species
This is a primitive group, closely resembling holosteans. Like eels, they have colourless, flattened larvae. Example:
Atlantic tarpon *Tarpon atlanticus*: found in tropical and sub-tropical waters. It can leap to a height of 6–7 ft

ORDER ANGUILLIFORMES
Eels; 300 species
Most eels are marine, but one family, the Anguillidae, spend most of their time as adults in rivers. Eel larvae are transparent and ribbon-like. The adults return to the spawning grounds when they are fully grown, and then generally die. Example:
European eel *Anguilla anguilla*: unlike most fish, it can survive out of water for considerable periods, having the ability to breathe through its skin

ORDER NOTACANTHIFORMES
Spiny eels; 20 species
Members of this order are long-bodied, deep-sea fish with tail fins and larvae like those of eels. Example:
Spiny eel *Lipogenys gilli*: found in the deep waters of the North Atlantic

ORDER CLUPEIFORMES
Herrings; 350 species
Most herrings are found in shoals near the surface of the sea, but many live in fresh water. The dorsal fin is placed near the centre of the body and the tail fin is deeply forked; the swim-bladder and the inner ear are closely connected. Example:
Atlantic herring *Clupea harengus*: found in the North Atlantic. Shoals of herrings make unpredictable seasonal migrations, as well as migrating to and from their spawning grounds

ORDER OSTEOGLOSSIFORMES
Arapaima and bony tongues; 16 species
These large, pike-like fish, found in the rivers of the tropics, have thick, ornamented scales and tooth-like tongue bones used in biting. Examples:
Arapaima *Arapaima gigas* (15 ft): found in South America. One of the largest freshwater fish, it weighs about 400 lb.
Bony tongue *Osteoglossum bicirrhosum*: found in South American rivers only, although fossilised relatives have been discovered in North America and Britain. It is believed to carry its eggs in its mouth until they hatch

ORDER MORMYRIFORMES
Mormyrids and gymnarchids; 150 species
These fish, closely related to the bony tongues and only found in Africa, also have toothed tongues. They are usually insect-eating and keep to fresh water. Many have a tube-like, down-curving snout, and all possess weak electric organs which enable them to locate anything within their electric field. Example:
Elephant snout fish *Mormyrus kanume*: found in the Nile and Lake Victoria. It uses its long, flexible snout to search between crevices for food

ORDER SALMONIFORMES
Salmon, pike and stomiatoids; 500 species
All salmon have a small, fleshy fin behind the dorsal fin, and deep-sea forms have light-producing organs. Examples:
Northern pike *Esox lucius* (3 ft 6 in.): found in fresh waters in Europe and North America
Stomiatoid *Stomias atriventer* (12 in.): found in deep waters in the Gulf of California and off the coast of Chile
Atlantic salmon *Salmo salar*: found in cold and temperate seas. It spends the first one to three years of its life in fresh waters, then migrates to the sea. After several years in the Atlantic, it returns to the same river in which it hatched. There, a 20 lb. female lays an average of 14,000 eggs, and then generally dies

ORDER MYCTOPHIFORMES
Lantern fish; 300 species
These deep-sea fish have light-producing organs along their sides. They live at depths down to 3500 ft, but feed at the surface. Some species have a fatty dorsal fin. Example:
Myctophum punctatum: found in the Atlantic and Mediterranean; it has large, sensitive eyes and its luminous organs may be a means of identification between members of the species

ORDER CTENOTHRISSIFORMES
There is one species:
Macristiid *Macristium chavesi*: the single surviving species of this order; found in deep waters of the South Atlantic. There are several fossil forms of these fish, which are related to the lantern fish

ORDER GONORHYNCHIFORMES
Milk fish; 15 species
These fish form a link between the macristiids and the carp. They have deeply forked tails and no teeth. Example:
Chanos chanos: found in the surface waters of the Indian Ocean. The female lays up to 9 million eggs at a time

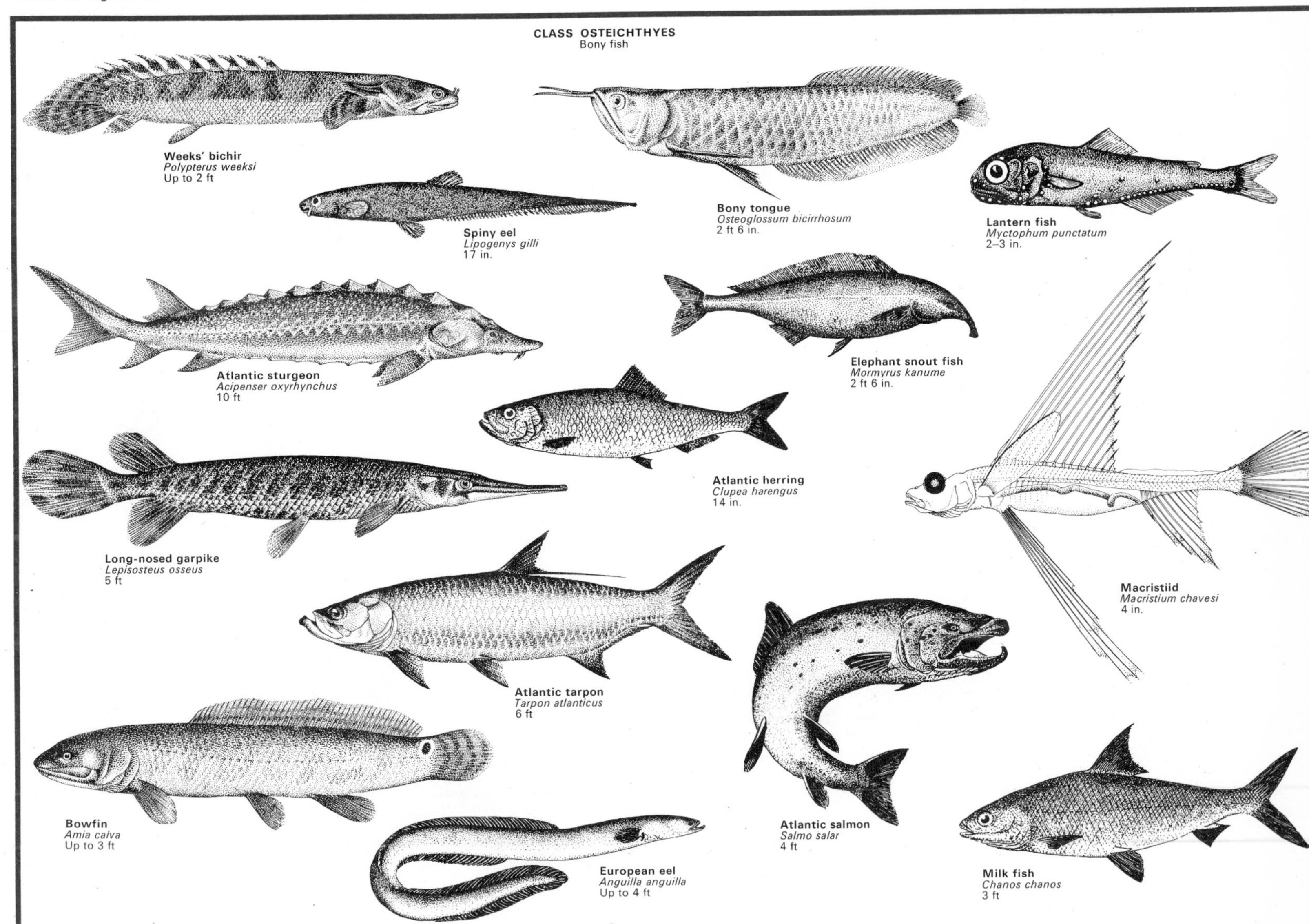

Fish

PHYLUM CHORDATA	Animals with notochords
SUB-PHYLUM VERTEBRATA	Animals with backbones
CLASS OSTEICHTHYES	Bony fish

ORDER CYPRINIFORMES
Carp, characins and gymnotids; 350 species
All members of this order, which contains the majority of freshwater fish, possess a series of small bones connecting the swim-bladder with the inner ear—an arrangement which probably increases the acuteness of their hearing. Most have scales on their bodies. Examples:
Electric eel *Electrophorus electricus* (5 ft): South American freshwater fish
Common carp *Cyprinus carpio*: originally found from the Black Sea to Turkestan, it has been introduced to and domesticated in many countries

ORDER SILURIFORMES
Catfish; 200 species
Most catfish are found in African, Asian and South American fresh waters, but some are marine, and some occur in northern fresh waters. The majority have barbels or feelers on the lower jaw and some species have a fleshy fin on the back. The inner ear and swim-bladder are connected, but the body is naked or covered only with bony plates. Example:
Armoured catfish *Corydoras aeneus*: South American freshwater fish

ORDER PERCOPSIFORMES
Sand rollers and pirate perches; 10 species
These minnow-like North American freshwater fish have spiny dorsal fins. Example:
Pirate perch *Aphredoderus sayanus*: found in fresh waters of the U.S.A.

ORDER BATRACHOIDIFORMES
Toadfish; 10 species
These predatory marine fish have large heads, strong teeth and long, tapering bodies. The front of the dorsal fin is spiny. Example:
Opsanus tau: found in shallow Atlantic waters. It has a special swim-bladder which it vibrates to make sounds

ORDER GOBIESOCIFORMES
Clingfish; 100 species
A large sucker, formed from pelvic fins, enables these small marine fish to cling to rocks in tide-pools. Example:
Tomicodon fasciatus: found in coastal waters of Brazil

ORDER LOPHIIFORMES
Anglers and frogfish; 150 species
Anglers have flat, squat bodies and huge heads with wide mouths. The first ray of the spiny dorsal fin has a flap of flesh at the end which acts as a fishing rod to lure prey. Some male angler fish are many times smaller than the females, to which they attach themselves. Although they still draw in water for respiration, they are completely dependent on their mates for nourishment. Example:
Whiskery angler *Antennarius scaber*: found in Atlantic waters. It has a well developed 'fishing rod'

ORDER GADIFORMES
Codfish and allies; 450 species
Codfish have long, tapering bodies. The dorsal and anal fins, which are usually without spines, may be divided into several parts. Example:
Atlantic cod *Gadus morhua*: found on both sides of the North Atlantic. Cod congregate in great shoals, especially at spawning time; about 400 million of them are caught each year

ORDER BERYCIFORMES
Squirrel fish and whalefish; 150 species
These deep-bodied fish have a series of spines in front of the dorsal and anal fins, and 18 or 19 rays on the tail fin. Example:
Striped squirrel fish *Holocentrus xantherythrus*: found near Pacific coral reefs

ORDER ATHERINIFORMES
Flying fish and killifish; 600 species
These small, slender, rather primitive teleosts with soft-rayed, spineless fins, are found in surface marine waters and fresh waters in the tropics. Example:
Flying fish *Oxyporhymphus micropterus*: found in the tropical Atlantic and Pacific. Its pectoral fins enable it to glide through the air for as much as 500 ft

ORDER ZEIFORMES
John Dory and allies; 60 species
These form a group of spiny-rayed, inshore, marine fish related to the squirrel fish; the tail fin has 11 to 14 rays. Example:
John Dory *Zeus faber*: found in the Atlantic. It has a thin body which enables it to approach prey undetected; when close enough it thrusts its jaws forward with a sudden snap

ORDER LAMPRIDIFORMES
Moonfish, earfish, ribbon-fish and mirrapinnids; 50 species
A group of deep-sea fish with protrusible jaws. The pelvic fins are placed at the front end of the scaleless body. Example:
Moonfish *Lampris guttatus*: widely distributed in the open seas. Its oval body is vertically flattened and weighs almost 600 lb. It eats squids and octopuses

ORDER GASTEROSTEIFORMES
Sticklebacks, seahorses and pipefish; 150 species
The fish in this group have elongated bodies encased in bony armour, and small mouths, often at the end of a tubular snout. Examples:
Three-spined stickleback *Gasterosteus aculeatus* (4 in.): found from the Arctic to temperate regions in both fresh and brackish water
Common American Atlantic seahorse *Hippocampus hudsonius*: found inshore. Female seahorses lay their eggs in brood pouches in the male's bodies, where they are incubated. Young seahorses also retreat to the pouch for the first few days following hatching

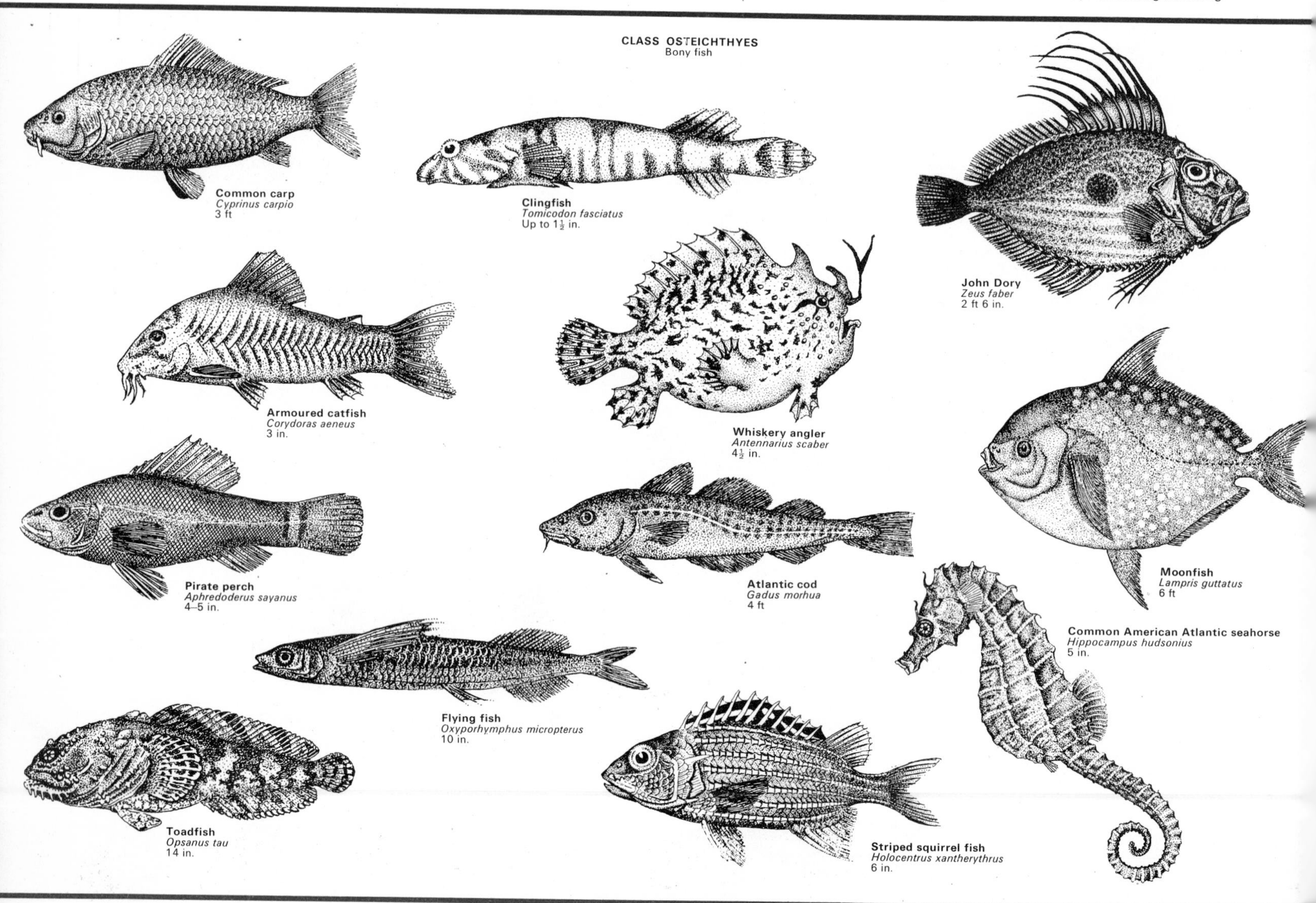

PHYLUM CHORDATA	Animals with notochords
SUB-PHYLUM VERTEBRATA	Animals with backbones
CLASS OSTEICHTHYES	Bony fish

ORDER CHANNIFORMES
Snakeheads; 5 species
These freshwater fish possess an extra lung-like respiratory organ which enables them to survive out of water for long periods. Example:
Ophicephalus striatus: found in rivers, ponds and marshes in Asia. It can survive droughts by burying itself in mud and becoming torpid

ORDER SYNBRANCHIFORMES
Swamp eels and cuchias; 7 species
A small group of coastal fish from south Asia and Africa which are not closely related to true eels; they have no paired fins and no scales. Example:
Cuchia *Amphipnous cuchia*: found in fresh and brackish waters in India and Burma. It breathes air and spends much time out of water in grass near the edges of ponds. It has two lung-like air sacs connected to the gill cavity

ORDER SCORPAENIFORMES
Scorpionfish, gurnards and bull-heads; 700 species
Well-developed bony ridges and spines on the head are the main characteristics of this group, which are often known as mail-cheeked fish. Examples:
Scorpionfish *Scorpaena cirrhosa* (10 in.): a tropical species found in the Indian and Pacific Oceans
Yellow gurnard *Trigla lucerna*: found inshore in the Atlantic

ORDER DACTYLOPTERIFORMES
Flying gurnards; 6 species
Long, wing-like pectoral fins enable these fish to glide through the water. Their heads are covered with bony plates. Example:
Dactylopterus orientalis: found in-shore in the Indo-Pacific region. The pectoral fins of this fish are even larger than those of the flying fish, although it cannot accomplish such long leaps

ORDER PEGASIFORMES
Dragonfish and sea moths; 4 species
This group of small, armoured fish, from the tropical Indo-Pacific region, have large, wing-like pectoral fins and small mouths beneath long snouts. Example:
Dragonfish *Pegasus draconis*: found among coral in shallow seas

ORDER PERCIFORMES
Perch and allies; 6500 species
This is the largest order of ray-finned fish. Many of its members bear spines on their fins. The tail fin has 17 rays and the scales often have serrated edges. Examples:
Discus fish *Symphysodon discus*: found in South American fresh waters
Blue-spotted argus *Cephalopholis argus* (18 in.): found near coral reefs in the Indian and Pacific Oceans
Common perch *Perca fluviatilis* (24 in.): found in Eurasian lakes, rivers and ponds
Mackerel *Scomber scomber* (up to 24 in.): found in the surface waters on both sides of the Atlantic
Remora *Echeneis naucrates* (2 ft 6 in.): found in tropical oceans, always associated with sharks or turtles

ORDER PLEURONECTIFORMES
Flatfish; 500 species
These fish spend most of their lives lying on their sides on the ocean bottom. After the juvenile stage one eye starts to move to the other side of the head so that eventually the fish has two eyes on the same side; from that time on the fish lies on its blind side. Sole, plaice and turbots lie on the left side, flounders on the right. Flatfish are derived from perches, but do not have hard fin spines. Example:
European plaice *Pleuronectes platessa*: found near the coasts of north-west Europe. It has the ability to blend into its surroundings, and can also hide by rapidly burrowing into mud or sand

ORDER TETRAODONTIFORMES
Triggerfish and pufferfish; 250 species
All have tiny mouths armed with heavy teeth, and short, deep bodies often covered with spines. The dorsal fin is spiny and the pelvic fins are either small or absent. Example:
Pufferfish *Spheroides spengleri*: found near coral reefs in tropical and sub-tropical regions of the Atlantic. It has spines instead of scales, and when the fish inflates itself these spines form an impenetrable barrier

SUB-CLASS SARCOPTERYGII
Fleshy-finned fish
The second sub-class of bony fish—the fleshy-finned fish—is the one which gave rise to amphibians. The fins are supported by large, fleshy lobes containing bony skeletons. There are two orders:

ORDER CROSSOPTERYGII
There is one species:
Coelacanth *Latimeria chalumnae*: the first live coelacanth was caught off South Africa in 1938. Until then, only fossils had been found and it was believed that the order had been extinct for 60 million years. It uses its heavy pectoral and pelvic fins to stir up the mud of the sea floor in search of prey

ORDER DIPNOI
Lungfish; 5 species
These fish belong to two families: the Ceratodidae, with a single Australian species, with heavy bodies, large scales, rayed fins and a single air-breathing lung; and the Lepidosirenidae of Africa and South America, which have slimmer bodies, smaller scales, rayless fins and obtain 95 per cent of their oxygen from the air through paired lungs. Example:
Australian lungfish *Neoceratodus forsteri*: unlike the African and South American family, this species does not build mud burrows to survive droughts; it dies rapidly if its river dries out

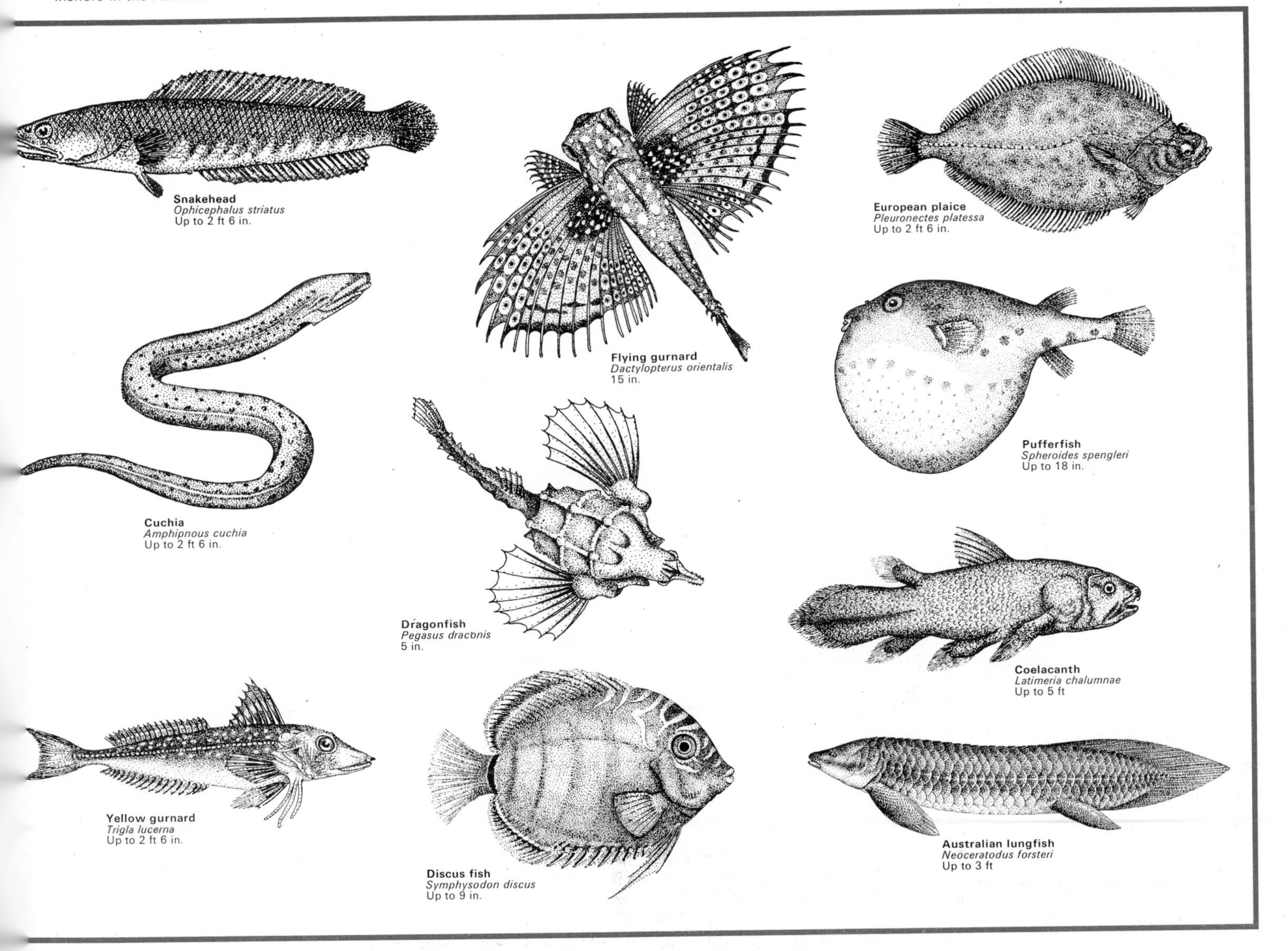

CLASSIFICATION

Amphibians

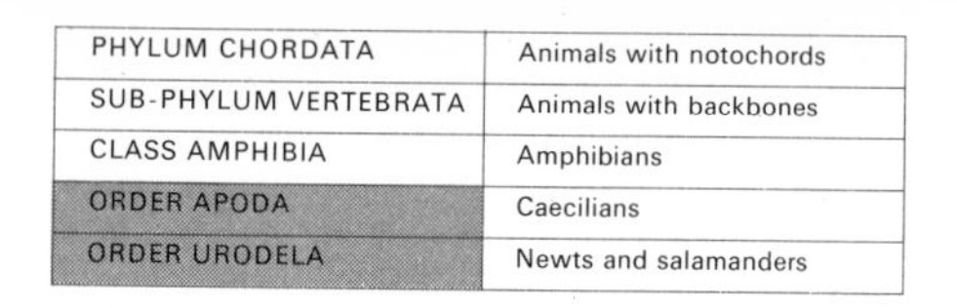

PHYLUM CHORDATA	Animals with notochords
SUB-PHYLUM VERTEBRATA	Animals with backbones
CLASS AMPHIBIA	Amphibians
ORDER APODA	Caecilians
ORDER URODELA	Newts and salamanders

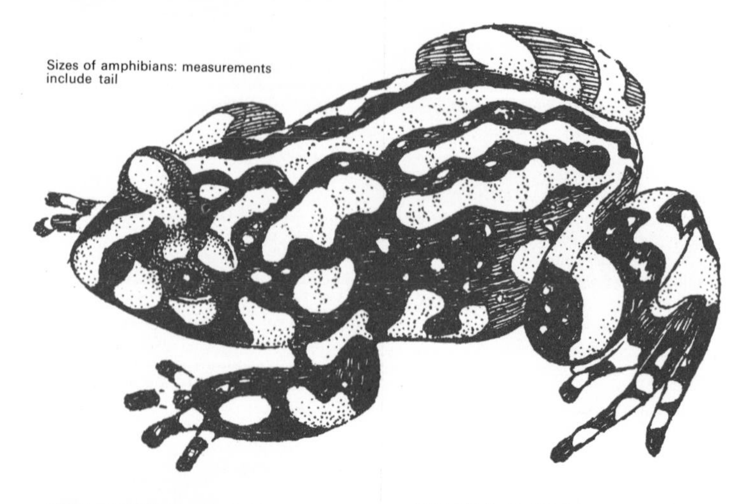

Sizes of amphibians: measurements include tail

Amphibians The most primitive class of land-living vertebrates, amphibians were the first group of vertebrate animals to emerge from an aquatic environment and live on land for much of their adult lives. Although in most cases the gill-breathing and aquatic young gradually change into lung or skin-breathing terrestrial adults, few amphibians are entirely independent of water, most requiring it at least for breeding. Amphibians are usually scaleless or have only small scales, and their skin—used in respiration—is generally moist. Their body fluids are easily lost through the thin skin, so most must remain in a damp environment. Like fish, amphibian larvae and aquatic adults have a lateral line, a pressure-sensitive organ which is of great use in water.

Amphibians evolved from an extinct sub-order of fleshy-finned fish called Rhipidistia. The main evolutionary changes involved the development of efficient lungs, the evolution of legs, the development of salivary glands and eyelids, and the elaboration of a double circulation. There are three living orders.

ORDER APODA

There is one family:

FAMILY CAECILIIDAE

Caecilians; 167 species

This is a little-known group of legless amphibians living in South America, tropical Africa, the Seychelles and south-east Asia. Their resemblance to earthworms is enhanced by their grooved skin, which gives an appearance of segmentation. They have large mucous glands on the lower part of each ring, 75–273 vertebrae and a small tentacle on each side of the face near the eye. Caecilians are internally fertilised, and some species bear live young; others lay eggs. They retain no traces of limb bones, or of pectoral or pelvic girdles. Example:

Panamanian caecilian *Caecilia ochrocephala*: lives in moist ground

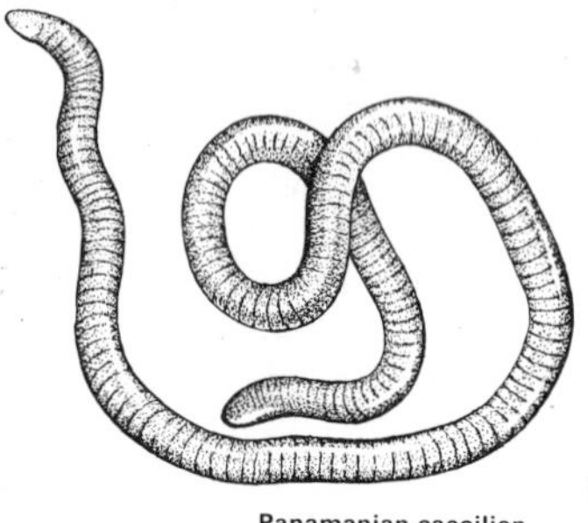

Panamanian caecilian
Caecilia ochrocephala
$6\frac{1}{2}$ in.

ORDER URODELA

Newts and salamanders

The skin of newts and salamanders is close-fitting, unlike that of frogs and toads. They possess limbs and have from 12 to more than 60 vertebrae; long, strong tails with muscles arranged in segments; and pectoral girdles made mainly of cartilage. The larvae have three pairs of external gills, and a few genera retain these throughout life. Some adult forms have neither gills nor lungs, but breathe only through the skin or the mouth. Fertilisation may be external or internal; most lay eggs. There are eight families:

FAMILY HYNOBIIDAE

Asiatic land salamanders; 30 species

Members of this family, found in eastern and central Asia, have movable eyelids. Some species live entirely on land. They are among the most primitive of the Urodela, and their eggs are fertilised externally. Example:

Siberian salamander *Ranodon sibiricus*: found in mountain streams in southern parts of central Asia

FAMILY CRYPTOBRANCHIDAE

Giant salamanders; 3 species

This is an aquatic family, whose members do not have movable eyelids. One species is found in the eastern U.S.A., the other two in China and Japan. Example:

Japanese giant salamander *Andrias japonicus*: the largest living amphibian. It lives in mountain brooks and is carnivorous, feeding on crabs, fish and snails

FAMILY AMBYSTOMIDAE

Mole salamanders; 32 species

All members of this family are found in North and Central America. Fertilisation is internal (as in all succeeding families of Urodela). Mole salamanders have rows of teeth across their palates. Examples:

Mexican axolotl *Ambystoma mexicanum* (female $8\frac{1}{2}$ in., male $5\frac{1}{4}$ in.): lives in lakes. It usually retains its larval form for life, but can change to a salamander if its habitat dries up

Marbled salamander *Ambystoma opacum*: found in the U.S.A. from New England south to northern Florida and west to Texas. It lives on hillsides near ponds and streams

FAMILY SALAMANDRIDAE

Newts and salamanders; 42 species

Newts have long rows of teeth in the roof of the mouth, and the adults never have gills. Examples:

Fire salamander *Salamandra salamandra* ($12\frac{1}{2}$ in.): found in the lowlands of Europe, North Africa and Asia Minor, living under roots and moss in moist areas. It hibernates in soil and breeds in running water, bearing live young

Smooth newt *Triturus vulgaris*: found in Europe and western Asia. The male has a crest along the back in the mating season, and its tail is vertically flattened for swimming. This newt hibernates on land

FAMILY AMPHIUMIDAE

Congo or lamper eels; 3 species

These small, blackish-green salamanders, with eel-like bodies and minute limbs, are found in swampy, stagnant water in the eastern parts of the U.S.A. Example:

Three-toed amphiuma *Amphiuma means tridactylum*: the female lays its eggs in a long string and incubates them

FAMILY PLETHODONTIDAE

Lungless salamanders; 183 species

Most of these are aquatic, but the adults have no gills except in one genus. The land-living species are less active and consume less oxygen than those living in mountain brooks, whose well aerated waters are suited to skin-breathing amphibians. Lungless salamanders are found in southern Europe, North and Central America and northern South America. Examples:

Texas blind salamander *Typhlomolge rathbuni* (3–4 in.): lives in water, 190 ft underground in San Marcos, Texas. It has permanent gills

Red-backed salamander *Plethodon cinereus*: lives in the eastern U.S.A. It is active at night and spends the day under logs and in crevices in rocks

FAMILY PROTEIDAE

Proteids; 6 species

Proteids are permanently larval in form, and lack eyelids. Example:

Mud-puppy *Necturus maculosus*: night-active in weedy North American streams. It eats a wide variety of aquatic animals

FAMILY SIRENIDAE

Sirens; 3 species

The members of this family, from southern U.S.A. and northern Mexico, have no hind limbs, teeth or eyelids. Their jaws are covered with horny plates and their gills persist throughout life. Example:

Greater siren *Siren lacertina*: found in south-eastern U.S.A. in shallow ponds and ditches. It swims like an eel, and burrows in soft mud

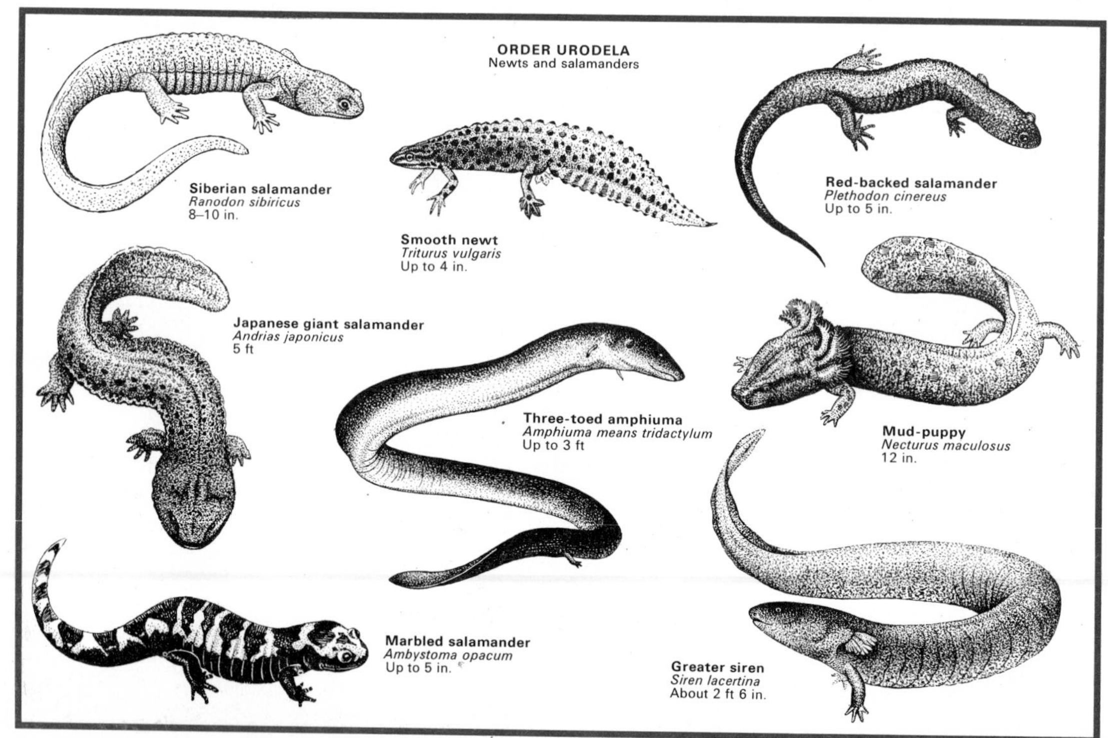

PHYLUM CHORDATA	Animals with notochords
SUB-PHYLUM VERTEBRATA	Animals with backbones
CLASS AMPHIBIA	Amphibians
ORDER ANURA	Frogs and toads

ORDER ANURA

Frogs and toads
The members of this group, the largest of the living orders of amphibians, have loosely fitting skins, no tails when adult, bony pectoral girdles, and usually no ribs. Fertilisation is always external, and no species remains larval for life. The anatomy is specialised for jumping: the vertebral column is short, with extensively fused vertebrae, the main bones of the limbs are fused, and the hind limbs are much longer than the forelimbs. Frogs and toads breathe by moving the floor of the mouth, first drawing air into the mouth and then forcing it into the lungs after closing the nostrils. There are 12 families:

FAMILY ASCAPHIDAE

Ascaphids; 4 species
Members of this family have ribs and rudimentary tail-wagging muscles. There are two genera, one in New Zealand and one in North America. Example:
Hochstetter's frog *Leiopelma hochstetteri*: lives under stones on the Coromandel Peninsula of the North Island of New Zealand

FAMILY PIPIDAE

Pipid toads; 15 species
These toads are entirely aquatic. Only the larvae have ribs. Both jaws are usually toothless, and all species are tongueless. Eyelids are sometimes present. Examples:
Surinam toad *Pipa pipa* (6 in.): found in Trinidad and South America as far south as the Mato Grosso in Brazil. Spawning takes place while the female is clasped by the male; he catches and fertilises the eggs, and then helps to squeeze them into the puffy skin on the female's back. The young emerge after about three months' incubation
African clawed toad *Xenopus laevis*: it has claws on three toes of its hind legs, some teeth in its upper jaw, and a tentacle under each eye. The female lays its eggs in still water and does not incubate them

FAMILY DISCOGLOSSIDAE

Discoglossids; 10 species
Discoglossids, found in Europe and Asia, have toothless lower jaws, and their ribs are present throughout life. Example:
Midwife toad *Alytes obstetricans*: found in Europe. The tadpoles hatch from spawn tangled round the male's thighs

FAMILY RHINOPHRYNIDAE

There is one species:
Mexican burrowing toad *Rhinophrynus dorsalis*: found among scrub and savanna on the coastal plains of Mexico and Guatemala

FAMILY PELOBATIDAE

Pelobatids; 54 species
These small toads with minute teeth are found in Eurasia, North Africa and North America. Example:
Iberian spadefoot toad *Pelobates cultripes*: found in south-western Europe and north-western Morocco

FAMILY BUFONIDAE

Toads; 300 species
The toads in this family have no upper teeth. There are several genera, the best known being *Bufo*, which contains 250 species and is found in all continents except Australia. These toads live on land and are active at dusk and before dawn. They are specialised for crawling and trap insects on their sticky tongues. Example:
Common toad *Bufo bufo*: found in Eurasia as far east as Lake Baikal; it lives a sedentary life under roots and logs. Its warty back secretes venom

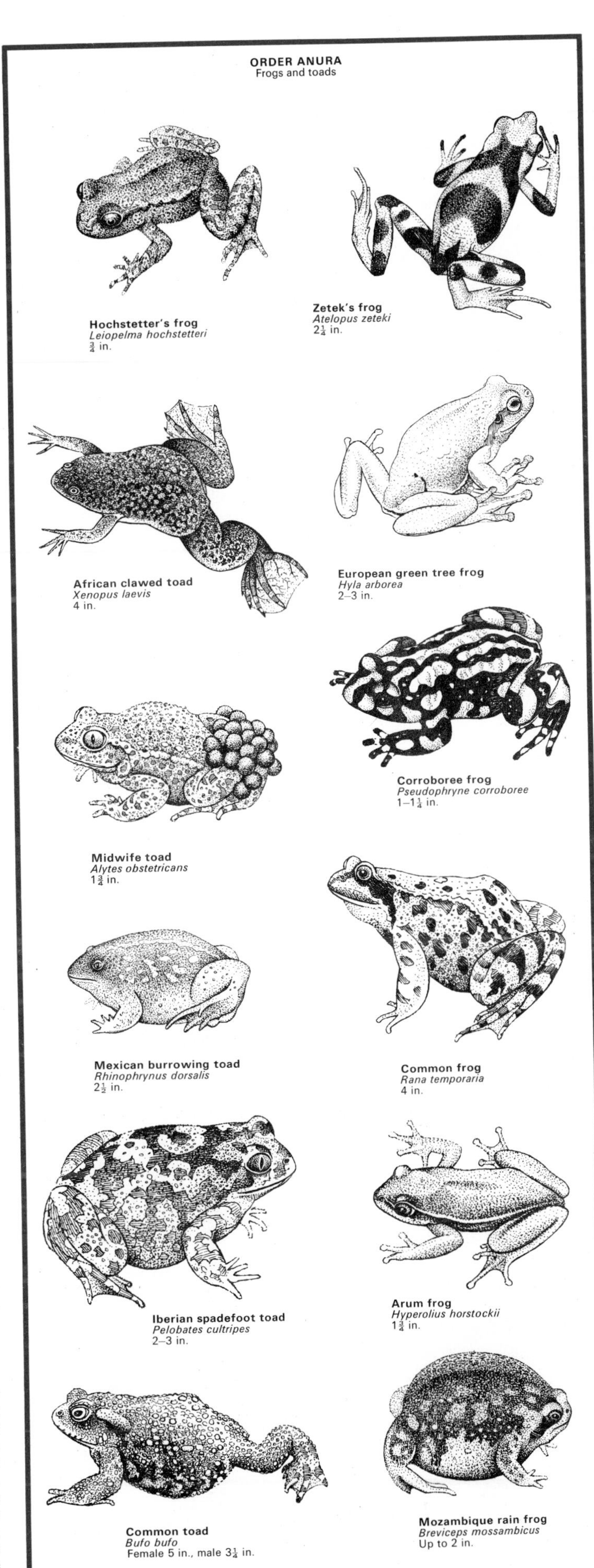

ORDER ANURA
Frogs and toads

Hochstetter's frog *Leiopelma hochstetteri* $\frac{3}{4}$ in.
Zetek's frog *Atelopus zeteki* $2\frac{1}{4}$ in.
African clawed toad *Xenopus laevis* 4 in.
European green tree frog *Hyla arborea* 2–3 in.
Midwife toad *Alytes obstetricans* $1\frac{3}{4}$ in.
Corroboree frog *Pseudophryne corroboree* $1–1\frac{1}{4}$ in.
Mexican burrowing toad *Rhinophrynus dorsalis* $2\frac{1}{2}$ in.
Common frog *Rana temporaria* 4 in.
Iberian spadefoot toad *Pelobates cultripes* 2–3 in.
Arum frog *Hyperolius horstockii* $1\frac{3}{4}$ in.
Common toad *Bufo bufo* Female 5 in., male $3\frac{1}{4}$ in.
Mozambique rain frog *Breviceps mossambicus* Up to 2 in.

FAMILY ATELOPODIDAE

Atelopodids; 26 species
There are only two genera in this family of small, brightly coloured frogs, which live near forest streams in Central and South America. Many species walk rather than hop. In one species, *Atelopus stelzneri* the tadpoles hatch within 24 hours of the eggs being laid. Example:
Zetek's frog *Atelopus zeteki*: lives near streams in Panama. It can neither swim nor jump very well, but its skin is poisonous and may deter predators

FAMILY HYLIDAE

Tree frogs; almost 600 species
Tree frogs are adapted for life in trees, and have an extra cartilage between the two end digits of the hands and feet, which gives them a better grip. The family, which also contains ground-living and aquatic forms, includes the large genus *Hyla*, containing 350 species, which is found throughout the world, except in Africa south of the Sahara and in eastern Polynesia. Example:
European green tree frog *Hyla arborea*: usually bright green but can rapidly change colour to yellow or slate grey

FAMILY LEPTODACTYLIDAE

Leptodactylids; 650 species
Members of this family are found in South and Central America, Australia and southern Africa. Several genera are adapted to the more arid areas of Australia. During the dry season they retire deep into the ground. Some species lay their eggs in burrows and rely on rainfall for development; the tadpoles' metamorphosis is so rapid that they become adults before the water evaporates. Example:
Corroboree frog *Pseudophryne corroboree*: lives in New South Wales in burrows beneath sphagnum moss in boggy country above the snow line

FAMILY RANIDAE

Frogs: hundreds of species
This group, which occurs on all continents, is unspecialised except for jumping—the specialisation common to all anurans. It includes the virtually world-wide genus *Rana*, containing 200–300 species, all of which have a notch on the end of the tongue. Some, such as the marsh frog *Rana ridibunda* and the edible frog *Rana esculenta*, are aquatic and have vocal sacs at the corner of the mouth; others have no vocal sacs. Example:
Common frog *Rana temporaria*: widespread in Eurasia, reaching the Arctic coast in places. The vocal sac is concealed under the skin of the throat

FAMILY RHACOPHORIDAE

Oar-legged frogs; hundreds of species
These frogs, found in the tropics of Africa, Madagascar and eastern Asia, resemble tree frogs in their adaptations to living in trees. They have webbed hind feet. Example:
Arum frog *Hyperolius horstockii*: found in southern Africa, where it often conceals itself within arum lilies

FAMILY MICROHYLIDAE

Microhylids; hundreds of species
This little-known family of burrowing and tree-living forms is found in the Old and New World tropics, except western Africa. The tadpoles hatch either at an advanced stage or completely metamorphosed. Example:
Mozambique rain frog *Breviceps mossambicus*: found in southern Africa. It burrows in open grassland and scrub at altitudes up to 4000 ft

CLASSIFICATION

Reptiles

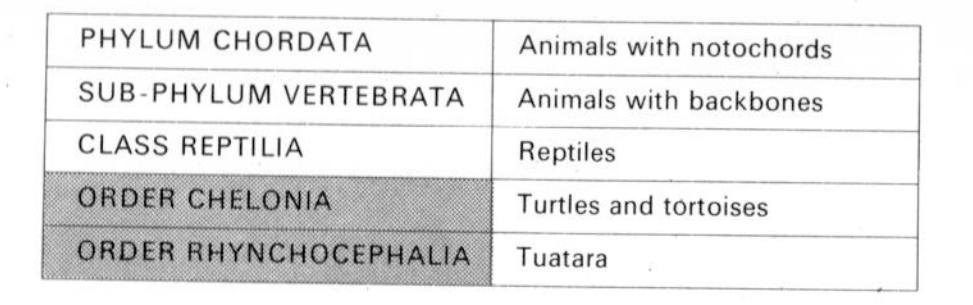

PHYLUM CHORDATA	Animals with notochords
SUB-PHYLUM VERTEBRATA	Animals with backbones
CLASS REPTILIA	Reptiles
ORDER CHELONIA	Turtles and tortoises
ORDER RHYNCHOCEPHALIA	Tuatara

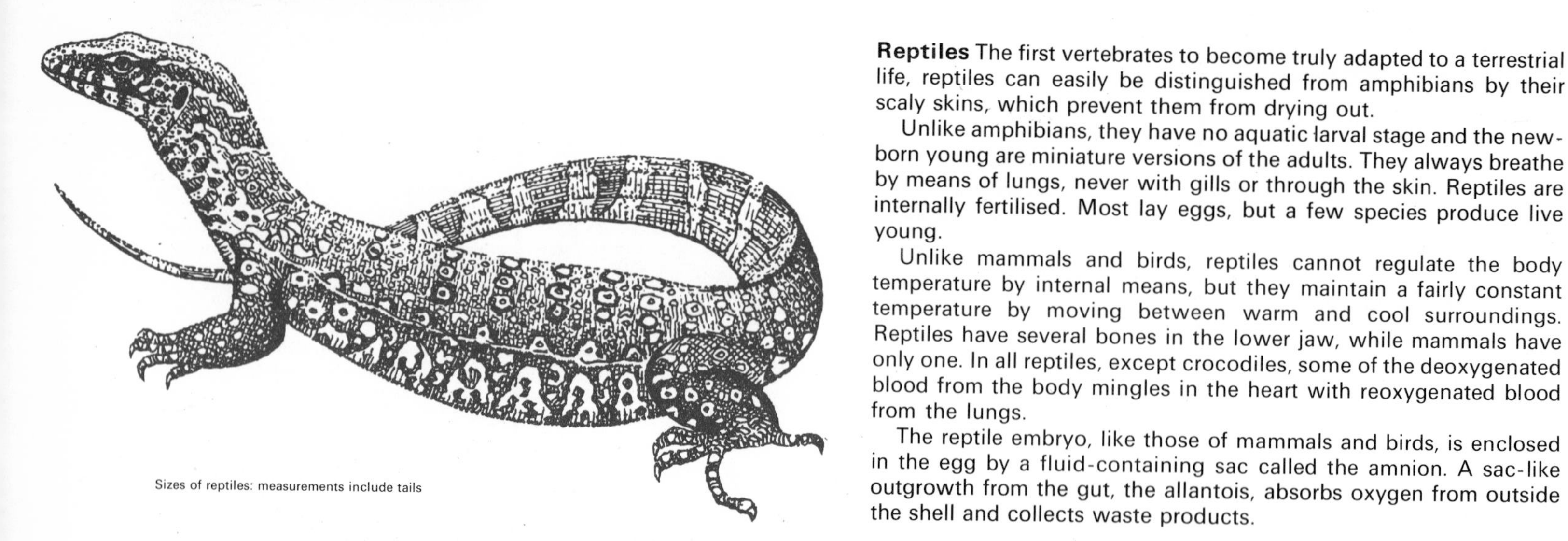

Sizes of reptiles: measurements include tails

Reptiles The first vertebrates to become truly adapted to a terrestrial life, reptiles can easily be distinguished from amphibians by their scaly skins, which prevent them from drying out.

Unlike amphibians, they have no aquatic larval stage and the new-born young are miniature versions of the adults. They always breathe by means of lungs, never with gills or through the skin. Reptiles are internally fertilised. Most lay eggs, but a few species produce live young.

Unlike mammals and birds, reptiles cannot regulate the body temperature by internal means, but they maintain a fairly constant temperature by moving between warm and cool surroundings. Reptiles have several bones in the lower jaw, while mammals have only one. In all reptiles, except crocodiles, some of the deoxygenated blood from the body mingles in the heart with reoxygenated blood from the lungs.

The reptile embryo, like those of mammals and birds, is enclosed in the egg by a fluid-containing sac called the amnion. A sac-like outgrowth from the gut, the allantois, absorbs oxygen from outside the shell and collects waste products.

ORDER CHELONIA

Turtles and tortoises
All the members of this primitive group, which has hardly changed in 200 million years, possess a shell of bony plates covered by horny scales. This forms an arched upper shell (the carapace) and an under-shell (the plastron). Their ribs, immobile and fused to the shell, cannot be used in breathing; the necessary pumping action is provided by the abdominal muscles. There are two sub-orders:

SUB-ORDER CRYPTODIRA

Hidden-necked turtles
The turtles in this group withdraw their heads into the shell by flexing the neck vertically. There are seven families:

FAMILY CHELYDRIDAE

Snapper, mud and musk turtles; 23 species
These turtles live on the bottom of ponds and rivers in warmer regions of the New World. Examples:
Eastern mud turtle *Kinosternon subrubrum* (4 in.): found in eastern North America. Its plastron is hinged
Common snapping turtle *Chelydra serpentina*: found in North America. It lies in wait for prey under water, and is also aggressive on land. It will eat anything it can catch

FAMILY DERMATEMYDIDAE

There is one species:
Central American river turtle *Dermatemys mawi*: little is known about this turtle, which lives in coastal rivers of Mexico and Guatemala

FAMILY TESTUDINIDAE

Tortoises and terrapins; 115 species
This family contains the most familiar land tortoises and freshwater turtles. Land tortoises are found in all the warmer parts of the world except Australia, and in all habitats from deserts to tropical forests and oceanic islands. Most species have blunt, heavily scaled feet and high-domed carapaces. Examples:
Painted terrapin *Chrysemys picta* (up to 7 in.): found in North America from southern Canada to the southern states of the U.S.A. It has a flat green shell, and a red streak near the ear. These terrapins, which are often kept as pets, are called 'turtles' in the U.S.A.
European pond tortoise *Emys orbicularis* (10 in.): lives mainly in southern Europe, but also occurs as far north as northern Germany
Leopard tortoise *Geochelone pardalis*: lives in southern and eastern Africa

FAMILY DERMOCHELYIDAE

There is one species:
Leathery turtle or **luth** *Dermochelys coriacea*: this 1200 lb. marine turtle lives in warm seas, but is rare. It feeds on jellyfish and tunicates, and breeds in the tropics. It has a smooth-backed appearance because its shell, unlike that of most turtles, consists of a mosaic of small bony plates embedded in skin. The shell is not joined to the ribs or the vertebrae

FAMILY CHELONIIDAE

Marine turtles; 5 species
These turtles live in the ocean and come ashore only to breed. The powerful front limbs are modified to form flippers, and the streamlined body narrows towards the back. The head cannot be withdrawn into the shell. Example:
Green turtle *Chelonia mydas*: lives in warm seas. Its Malaysian breeding grounds are protected. It may weigh 1000 lb.

FAMILY TRIONYCHIDAE

Soft-shelled turtles; 22 species
These highly aquatic animals, from the fresh waters of North America, Asia and Africa, have no horny scales. They have partly webbed hind feet. Example:
Eastern soft-shelled turtle *Trionyx spiniferus*: found in eastern North America, it feeds on water insects and crayfish

FAMILY CARETTOCHELIDAE

There is one species:
New Guinea pitted-shelled turtle *Carettochelys insculpta*: this very rare turtle lives in rivers. It has a complete bony shell, but no covering of horny scales. It has paddle-shaped limbs

SUB-ORDER PLEURODIRA

Side-necked turtles
These turtles withdraw their heads into the shell by bending the neck sideways. There are two families:

SUB-ORDER CRYPTODIRA
Hidden-necked turtles

Leathery turtle or luth
Dermochelys coriacea
Nearly 7 ft

Common snapping turtle
Chelydra serpentina
Up to 14 in.

Green turtle
Chelonia mydas
4 ft

Central American river turtle
Dermatemys mawi
12 in.

Eastern soft-shelled turtle
Trionyx spiniferus
Up to 16 in.

Leopard tortoise
Geochelone pardalis
23 in.

New Guinea pitted-shelled turtle
Carettochelys insculpta
Up to 20 in.

FAMILY CHELIDAE

Snake-necked turtles; 31 species
This group is found in South America, Australia and New Guinea. Example:
Australian snake-necked turtle *Chelodina longicollis*: lives in eastern Australian rivers and feeds on fish

FAMILY PELOMEDUSIDAE

Pelomedusid turtles; 14 species
These turtles, from South America, Africa and Madagascar, bend their necks sideways like the snake-necks, but their necks are hidden by skin when they are withdrawn. Example:
Podocnemis unifilis: lives in South American rivers

SUB-ORDER PLEURODIRA
Side-necked turtles

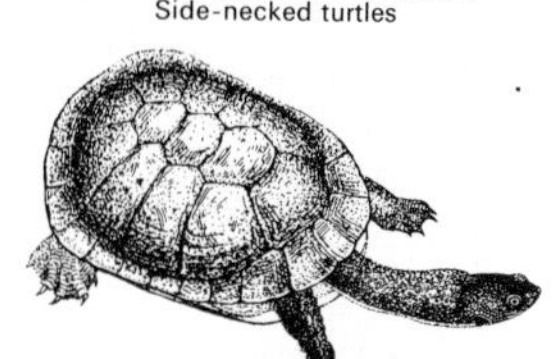

Australian snake-necked turtle
Chelodina longicollis
12 in.

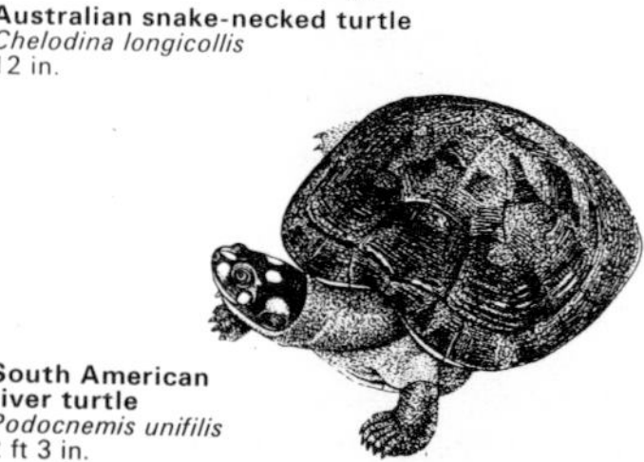

South American river turtle
Podocnemis unifilis
2 ft 3 in.

ORDER RHYNCHOCEPHALIA

There is only one surviving species in this order, the others having become extinct 100 million years ago. This species, which forms the family Sphenodontidae, is:
Tuatara *Sphenodon punctatus*: once found throughout New Zealand, now lives only on small islands off the coast of the North Island. This primitive, lizard-like reptile has teeth fused to the edges of the jaws (not set in sockets), a rudimentary third eye on top of the head and no copulatory organ

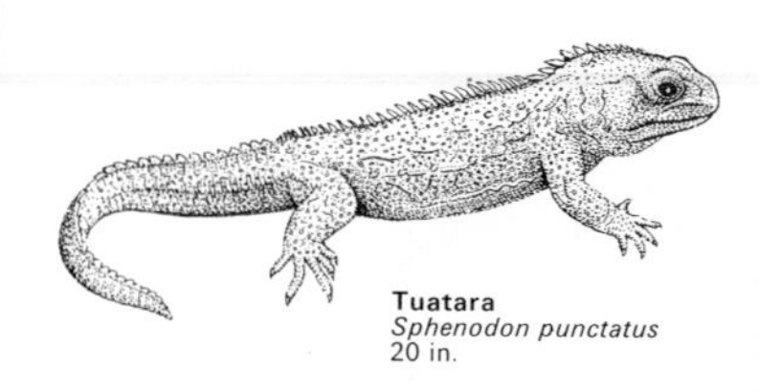

Tuatara
Sphenodon punctatus
20 in.

PHYLUM CHORDATA	Animals with notochords
SUB-PHYLUM VERTEBRATA	Animals with backbones
CLASS REPTILIA	Reptiles
ORDER SQUAMATA	Lizards and snakes

ORDER SQUAMATA

Lizards and snakes

Members of this order, the most successful group of modern reptiles, have bodies covered with small overlapping scales. There may be a single row of broad scales along the belly, and the head often has well-defined scales, sometimes containing bony plates fused to the skull. The tongue is notched or forked, the teeth are fused to the rims of the jaws. Some lizards are legless, like snakes.

The females usually lay eggs with parchment-like shells, but some hatch the eggs in their bodies. There are two sub-orders, whose members are not always easily distinguishable:

SUB-ORDER LACERTILIA

Lizards

Many lizards are snake-like in appearance with small limbs, or no limbs at all, and small eyes and ears. Some families consist entirely of limbless forms, and many others have some limbless members. A few lizards—some skinks, for example—give birth to live young. Some forms can shed the tail and regenerate it, but the new tail lacks the original pattern and has a cartilaginous rod instead of vertebrae. The skin is shed in pieces, and many lizards can change colour, if only slightly. There are 20 families:

FAMILY GEKKONIDAE

Geckos; 400 species

These lizards are usually nocturnal and have big eyes, generally covered by a transparent membrane which is cleaned with the tongue. Their digits are short, usually with large, backward-curved claws, and most geckos have hair-like filaments on the undersides of their digits which can hook on to irregularities on vertical surfaces as smooth as glass. They are the only lizards with well-developed voices. Example:

Tokay gecko *Gekko gecko*: a south-east Asian gecko, named after its cry. It feeds on insects and mice

FAMILY PYGOPODIDAE

Flap-footed lizards; 13 species

These snake-like lizards from Australasia lack forelimbs and have flap-like hind limbs. Example:

Sharp-snouted snake-lizard *Lialis burtoni*: found in savanna in Australia and New Guinea

FAMILY XANTUSIIDAE

Night lizards; 11 species

These nocturnal lizards with gecko-like eye membranes hide by day in crevices in rocks and logs. They are found in Central America and south-western North America. Example:

Granite night lizard *Xantusia henshawi*: lives in California and Mexico, and feeds at night on insects, spiders, scorpions and centipedes. It bears live young

FAMILY IGUANIDAE

Iguanas; about 700 species

Iguanas have teeth on the inner sides of their jaws. There are long-legged, often swift-running forms, and some have a scaly crest on their backs. They occur mainly in the New World, but also in Madagascar, the Galapagos Islands, Fiji and Tonga. Examples:

Green anole *Anolis carolinensis* (9 in.): known as 'chameleon' in North America. It is brightly coloured and swift-moving, and can change colour rapidly, like the true chameleons

Common iguana *Iguana iguana*: lives in the trees of South American tropical forests

FAMILY AGAMIDAE

Agamid lizards; about 300 species

The agamid lizards are the counterparts in Europe, Africa, Asia and Australia of the iguanas, and closely resemble them, except that their teeth are borne on the rims of the jaws. Like iguanas, some forms have high crests supported by vertebral spines. Some species have throat sacs, some have spiny tails, some have spiny skins, and some have frills and run on their hind legs. Example:

Starred agama or **hardun** *Agama stellio*: lives in Greece, Asia Minor and Egypt in mountainous or rocky country

FAMILY CHAMAELEONTIDAE

Chameleons; 85 species

The feet of these tree-living lizards are adapted to grasping by having two toes opposed to the other three. Chameleons also have grasping tails. Their eyes move independently and their fused eyelids admit light through a small hole in the middle. The skull is crested, and the sticky tongue, which is half as long as the animal, shoots out to catch insects. Some members of the genus *Chamaeleo*, which contains 73 of the 85 species, have flamboyant horns. Example:

Common chameleon *Chamaeleo chamaeleon*: found in southern Spain, North Africa and Palestine

FAMILY DIBAMIDAE

Burrowing lizards; 4 species

Found in Indo-China and from the Philippines to New Guinea, and in Mexico, these short-tailed lizards are blind and earless, and are either limbless or have small limbs. Example:

Dibamus novae-guineae: lives in New Guinea, often in rotting logs

FAMILY SCINCIDAE

Skinks; about 700 species

The bodies of skinks tend to be elongated, and their limbs are small and sometimes absent, as are their ear apertures. They burrow in sand or live in leaf litter. The family includes the genus *Eumeces*, comprising 59 species, found in North and Central America, Asia and North Africa. These have longer legs than other skinks, and live in steppe and stony desert. About half the species lay eggs; the others bear live young. Example:

Australian blue-tongued skink *Tiliqua scincoides*: feeds on leaves, fruit and earthworms. It can withstand a wide range of temperatures

FAMILY FEYLINIIDAE

Limbless skinks; 4 species

These termite-eaters from equatorial Africa and Madagascar are entirely without legs. Example:

Feylinia currori: found in equatorial Africa, under decaying logs. It feeds almost exclusively on termites

FAMILY GERRHOSAURIDAE

Plated lizards; 25 species

Found in the dry areas of Africa and Madagascar, these lizards have armour-like scales. Example:

Sudan plated lizard *Gerrhosaurus major*: digs tunnels several feet long

FAMILY CORDYLIDAE

Girdle-tailed lizards; 23 species

These lizards are found in the grasslands of eastern and southern Africa. Members of the genus *Platysaurus* have flattened bodies, enabling them to shelter in rock crevices. Example:

Giant girdle-tailed lizard or **sungazer** *Cordylus giganteus*: a South African spiny lizard. It flattens itself to the ground in defence, protecting its underparts and exposing only its spiny upper surface

FAMILY LACERTIDAE

African and Eurasian lizards; about 150 species

These small, agile lizards have very long fragile tails and head shields which are fused to the bones of the skull. Examples:

Viviparous lizard *Lacerta vivipara* (6 in.): found in northern and central Eurasia; it is the only lizard to live within the Arctic circle. It produces live young

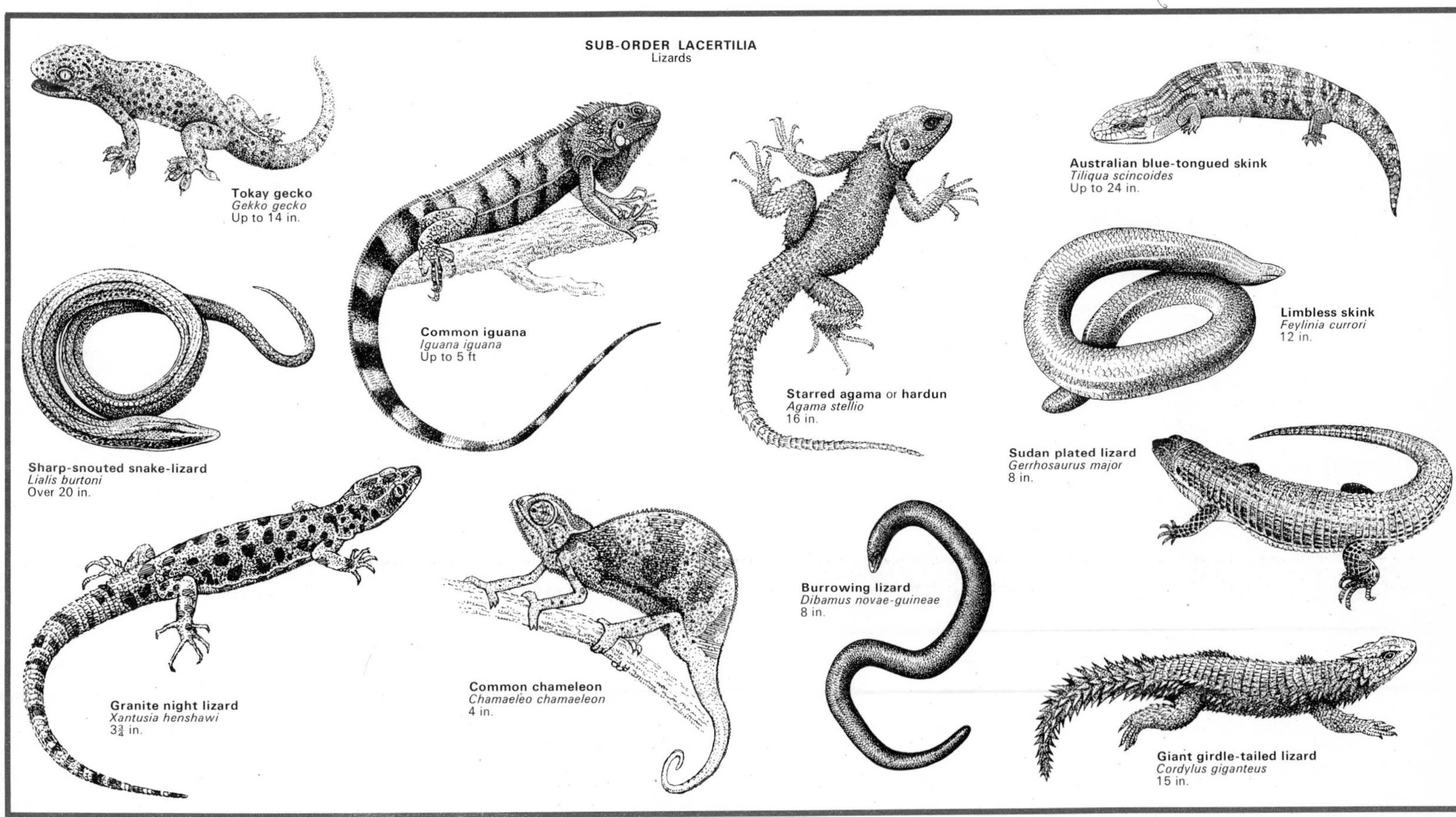

CLASSIFICATION

Reptiles

PHYLUM CHORDATA	Animals with notochords
SUB-PHYLUM VERTEBRATA	Animals with backbones
CLASS REPTILIA	Reptiles
ORDER SQUAMATA	Lizards and snakes

Wall-lizard *Lacerta muralis* (8 in.): found from central Europe to northern Asia and Asia Minor. It is marked with lines and spots which harmonise with surroundings such as walls and debris where it spends much of its time
Eyed lizard *Lacerta lepida*: found in southern Europe and north-western Africa. It preys on mice, snakes and other lizards

FAMILY TEIIDAE
South American lizards or tegus; about 200 species
Tegus are the New World counterparts of the Lacertidae, but their head shields are separate from their skull bones. Example:
Common tegu *Tupinambus teguixin*: found in tropical America. It feeds on insects, worms and rodents

FAMILY ANGUIDAE
Slow worms; 40 species
These lizards are found in the New World, Europe and parts of Asia; they have fragile tails and forked tongues. Some species are completely legless. Example:
Slow worm *Anguis fragilis*: occurs from 60° N in Europe southwards to North Africa and in western Asia. It feeds on soft-bodied prey, such as slugs and earthworms

FAMILY ANNIELLIDAE
Legless lizards; 2 species
These Californian lizards are found in sandy ground, in which they catch their insect prey. They are small burrowers with no limbs or external ears, and small eyes. Example:
Californian legless lizard *Anniella pulchra*: a silvery or silver-black lizard which feeds on insects

FAMILY XENOSAURIDAE
Xenosaurid lizards; 4 species
This is a little-known group. All species have strong legs and robust bodies covered in a mixture of large and small scales. There are three species in Central America and one in China. Example:
Chinese crocodile-lizard *Shinisaurus crocodilurus*: lives near streams in China and feeds on tadpoles and fish

FAMILY HELODERMATIDAE
Venomous lizards; 2 species
These are the only poisonous lizards. The venom glands are in the lower jaw, not in the upper jaw as in snakes. Example:
Gila monster *Heloderma suspectum*: found in northern Mexico and south-western states of the U.S.A. A venomous lizard which preys mainly on small rodents; its bite is rarely fatal to man

FAMILY LANTHANOTIDAE
There is one species:
Earless monitor *Lanthanotus borneensis*: found in Borneo. It has short legs and its lower eyelids have a clear window

FAMILY VARANIDAE
Monitors; 24 species
All these large lizards belong to the genus *Varanus*, found throughout the warmer regions of the Old World. They are swift-moving predators. Examples:
Komodo dragon *Varanus komodoensis* (up to 12 ft): this, the largest lizard, was not discovered by Europeans until 1912. It lives only on some of the Lesser Sunda Islands of Indonesia
Nile monitor *Varanus niloticus*: lives near rivers in Africa. It feeds on frogs, birds, crocodiles' eggs and small lizards

FAMILY AMPHISBAENIDAE
Worm-lizards; 120 species
This is a family of burrowing, legless lizards with short, thick tails. The small head is not marked off from the body, so both ends look similar—hence the family's scientific name ('going both ways'). They are found in Florida, Mexico, South America, the Mediterranean and Africa. Example:
White-bellied worm-lizard *Amphisbaena alba*: lives in tropical America. Often found on manure heaps, it feeds on ants and termites

SUB-ORDER LACERTILIA
Lizards

Eyed lizard *Lacerta lepida* Over 24 in.
Chinese crocodile-lizard *Shinisaurus crocodilurus* 10–15 in.
Gila monster *Heloderma suspectum* 20 in.
Common tegu *Tupinambus teguixin* Up to 4 ft
Earless monitor *Lanthanotus borneensis* 17 in.
Nile monitor *Varanus niloticus* 6 ft
Slow worm *Anguis fragilis* 20 in.
White-bellied worm-lizard *Amphisbaena alba* 24 in.
Californian legless lizard *Anniella pulchra* 8–10 in.

SUB-ORDER SERPENTES
Snakes
Most snakes, unlike lizards, are adapted to swallow prey larger than themselves; flexible ligaments and joints allow the two parts of the lower jaw to move apart during swallowing and give them some independence of movement. Snakes are always legless, and their skin is usually shed whole. The tail does not regenerate if lost; the eyelids are fused to form a transparent covering. The left lung is usually reduced in size, while the right lung is greatly enlarged and elongated. In many forms the forked tongue is protruded and retracted constantly through a notch in the snout, without the mouth being opened. Snakes probably evolved from burrowing lizards, and burrowing snakes, like lizards, appear to have evolved several times. Venomous snakes predominate only in Australia. There are 11 families:

FAMILY ANOMALEPIDAE
Anomalepid snakes; about 20 species
This is a small tropical South American group of blind snakes, with large head shields. Example:
Helminthophis bondensis: this snake burrows in South American forest floors

FAMILY TYPHLOPIDAE
Blind snakes; 150 species
This is the commonest burrowing family. The skull is rigid and the front of the head has a single plate for pushing through earth. The body is cylindrical, and the very short tail ends in a spine. There are no teeth in the lower jaw; and the eyes are tiny and often do not function. These snakes, which come to the surface after heavy rain, feed on earthworms and millipedes. They are found in southern Eurasia, Africa, Madagascar, tropical parts of the Americas and Australia. Example:
Spotted blind snake *Typhlops punctatus*: lives in African equatorial forests

FAMILY LEPTOTYPHLOPIDAE
Blind or thread snakes; 40 species
These blind snakes, with large teeth in the lower jaw and none in the upper, are found in Africa and tropical America. Example:
Western blind snake *Leptotyphlops humilis*: this burrowing snake is found in south-western U.S.A. and Mexico

FAMILY UROPELTIDAE
Shield-tailed snakes; 43 species
These small, primitive burrowers from India and Ceylon have a large shield-like scale at the end of the tail. They do not lay eggs, but give birth to about six live young. Example:
Uropeltis ocellatus: burrows in soft ground in the Indian forests

FAMILY ANILIIDAE
Pipe snakes; 10 species
Members of this small family of burrowers, from South America and south-east Asia, still have vestiges of hind limbs. They prey on other snakes. Example:
Flower-pot snake *Typhlops braminus* (4 in.): found in Mexico, Madagascar, south-east Asia and many Pacific islands. It lives among the roots of plants and feeds on insect larvae and other small soil-dwelling animals
Cylindrophis rufus: lives in south-east Asia. It is cylindrical, but flattens itself when disturbed

FAMILY XENOPELTIDAE
There is one species:
Sunbeam snake *Xenopeltis unicolor*: found in south-east Asia. A burrower with iridescent brown scales, it preys on other snakes. The teeth of its lower jaw are set in a loosely hinged bone

FAMILY BOIDAE
Constrictors; about 70 species
These large, non-poisonous snakes often have claws, which are vestigial hind limbs, and sometimes they have two

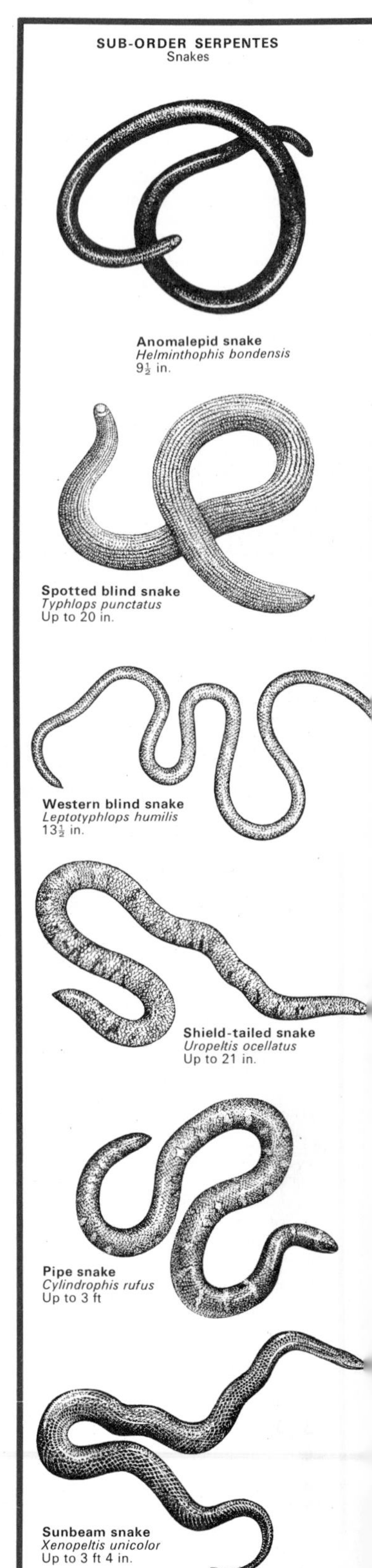
SUB-ORDER SERPENTES
Snakes

Anomalepid snake *Helminthophis bondensis* 9½ in.
Spotted blind snake *Typhlops punctatus* Up to 20 in.
Western blind snake *Leptotyphlops humilis* 13½ in.
Shield-tailed snake *Uropeltis ocellatus* Up to 21 in.
Pipe snake *Cylindrophis rufus* Up to 3 ft
Sunbeam snake *Xenopeltis unicolor* Up to 3 ft 4 in.

PHYLUM CHORDATA	Animals with notochords
SUB-PHYLUM VERTEBRATA	Animals with backbones
CLASS REPTILIA	Reptiles
ORDER SQUAMATA	Lizards and snakes
ORDER CROCODILIA	Crocodiles

fully developed lungs. They kill their prey by constriction: the snake coils its body round its victim and squeezes, causing suffocation. Nearly all constrictors are found in the tropics. The largest species, the reticulated python *Python reticulatus* occasionally grows to 33 ft. Examples:

Boa constrictor *Boa constrictor* (11 ft): found in dry forests and scrub in South America. It lives in tree-holes, among tree roots and in holes in the ground. It is rarely found in water, and it preys mainly on small mammals and rats

SUB-ORDER SERPENTES
Snakes

Indian python
Python molurus
Up to 20 ft

Elephant's trunk snake
Acrochordus javanicus
Up to 6 ft

Puff adder
Bitis arietans
3–4 ft

King cobra or **hamadryad**
Ophiophagus hannah
18 ft

Grass snake
Natrix natrix
Female up to 6 ft

Anaconda *Eunectes murinus* (25 ft): lives in swamps and slow-moving rivers in the Amazon forests. It stays under water for long periods, and may burrow in mud when the water dries up. Peccaries, deer, caymans and fish are its main prey

Indian python *Python molurus*: found in India and south-east Asia. It has spear-head markings on the head and neck

FAMILY ACROCHORDIDAE

Oriental water snakes; 2 species

These snakes are well adapted to life in estuaries and coastal waters, with nostrils on top of the snout, and small eyes. They give birth to about 30 live young at a time. Example:

Elephant's trunk snake *Acrochordus javanicus*: found from India to northern Australia. The female is heavy-bodied, and much larger than the male

FAMILY VIPERIDAE

Vipers; 100 species

The viper has tubular fangs at the front of the mouth, folded back when the jaw is closed, but erect when it is open; they are so long that the viper need only strike, and not chew, its victim. The venom runs down a canal in each fang, and is more potent just after the snake sheds its skin. It primarily affects the circulatory system of the victim and causes swelling, inflammation and haemorrhage. There is only a vestige of a reduced lung, and often no trace of it at all. The family includes the rattlesnakes of the genera *Crotalus* and *Sistrurus* whose modified tail skin vibrates to produce a warning. Rattlesnakes are members of the group known as pit-vipers because they possess heat-sensitive organs located in pits between the eyes and the nostrils. Pit-vipers are found mainly in America, whereas true vipers, which lack facial pits, live in the Old World. Examples:

Common adder or **viper** *Vipera berus* (up to 30 in.) found in northern Eurasia in forests, tundra and heath. Its poison acts quickly on small rodents, but is too mild to cause many fatalities to man

Eastern diamond-back rattlesnake *Crotalus adamanteus* (8 ft): abundant in Florida in moist ground. It swims well

Puff adder *Bitis arietans*: found in Africa. Highly venomous, it is fat and sluggish and one of the longest vipers

FAMILY ELAPIDAE

Cobras, mambas, coral snakes and sea-snakes; about 200 species

All these snakes are highly poisonous. The grooved or tubular fangs at the front of the mouth are not very long, so the poison must be injected by chewing. The venom affects mainly the nervous system, and does not usually produce local effects. The sea-snakes usually give birth to live young, but the land forms usually lay eggs. Examples:

Black-and-yellow sea-snake *Pelamis platurus* (up to 3 ft): lives in tropical seas. It has a vertically flattened tail and a long flexible body

King cobra or **hamadryad** *Ophiophagus hannah*: lives in south-east Asia. It is one of the largest poisonous snakes, but is seldom aggressive to man. The female buries her eggs in leaves, then coils herself above them. It feeds mainly on monitor lizards and other snakes

FAMILY COLUBRIDAE

Colubrid snakes; about 1100 species

This family has the most species and its members are found throughout the world. Most are harmless; some have poison, but the small fangs at the back of the jaw are rarely harmful to large mammals. There are no traces of hind limbs, and the left lung is small or absent. Examples:

Boomslang *Dispholidus typus* (up to 6 ft): a green snake found in African savanna. It is the only colubrid whose bite may be fatal to man

Grass snake *Natrix natrix*: found in Europe, parts of North Africa and eastwards to central Asia

ORDER CROCODILIA

Crocodiles

The closest living relatives of the dinosaurs, these large reptiles are adapted to an aquatic existence. A fold of skin closes the windpipe at the back, so that the animal can open its mouth under water and breathe with its nostrils above the surface. The nostrils, like the eyes and ears, are placed high on the head. When crocodiles are completely submerged, the ears and nostrils are closed by valves, and the eyes covered by membranes. Crocodiles have no salivary glands and usually eat under water. Some species sweep their prey from the land into the water with their powerful, vertically flattened tails. Crocodiles' scales are hard and square, and a few rows of raised scales down the back and tail contain knobs of bone. There are two families:

FAMILY GAVIALIDAE

There is one species:

Gavial or **gharial** *Gavialis gangeticus*: also known as the true or Indian gavial, it lives in the Indus, Ganges and Brahmaputra river systems, feeding on fish. It has very small nasal bones, 27–29 teeth on each side, and a long narrow snout that widens at the nostrils

FAMILY CROCODYLIDAE

Crocodiles; 20 species

Crocodiles live mainly in tropical rivers, though some forms swim out to sea. There are three sub-families. The Alligatorinae sub-family includes the alligators and caymans, which have 17–22 teeth on each side of each jaw; the fourth tooth of the lower jaw fits into a pit in the upper jaw and is invisible when the mouth is closed. In the Crocodylinae, the true crocodiles, with 14 or 15 teeth on each side, the fourth tooth fits into a pit in the upper jaw, but remains visible when the mouth is closed. This tooth is also visible in the Tomistominae, the false gavials; these have 20 or 21 teeth a side. Example:

Nile crocodile *Crocodylus niloticus*: found in southern and central Africa and Madagascar. It lives in lairs dug out of river banks and feeds mainly on fish, though it also eats land animals

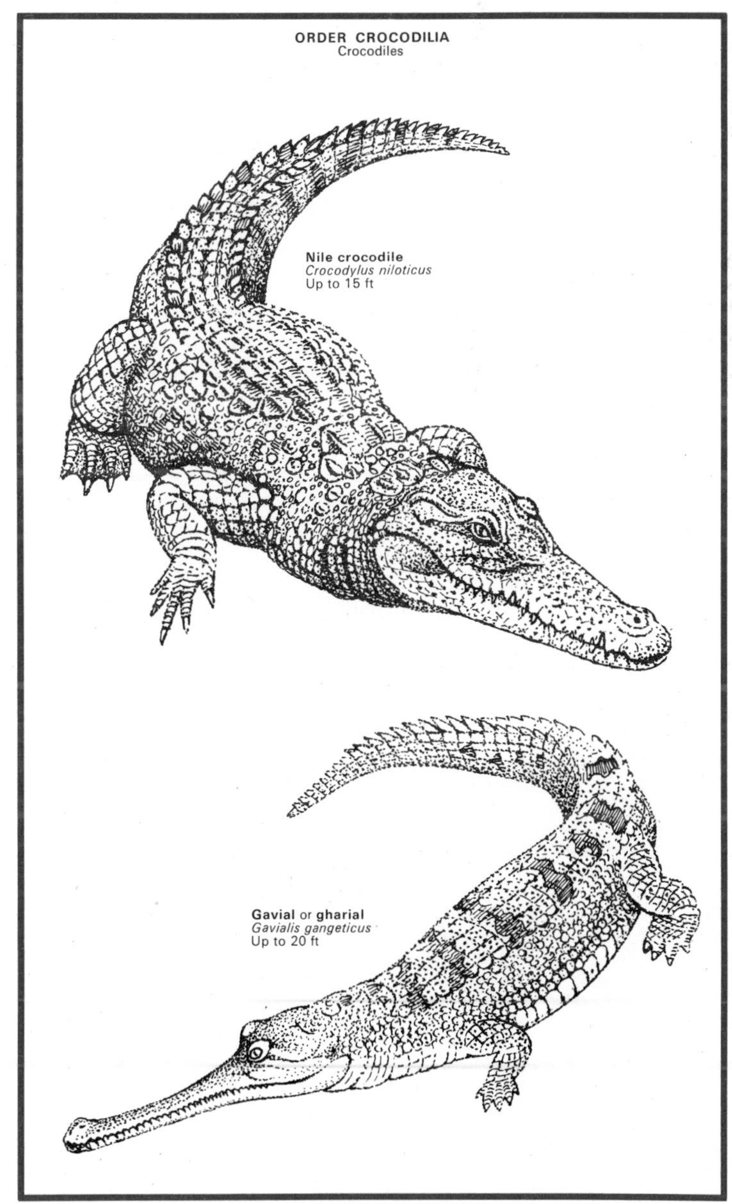

ORDER CROCODILIA
Crocodiles

Nile crocodile
Crocodylus niloticus
Up to 15 ft

Gavial or **gharial**
Gavialis gangeticus
Up to 20 ft

CLASSIFICATION

Birds

PHYLUM CHORDATA	Animals with notochords
SUB-PHYLUM VERTEBRATA	Animals with backbones
CLASS AVES	Birds
ORDER APTERYGIFORMES	Kiwis
ORDER STRUTHIONIFORMES	Ostrich
ORDER RHEIFORMES	Rheas
ORDER CASUARIIFORMES	Cassowaries and emus
ORDER TINAMIFORMES	Tinamous
ORDER PODICIPEDIFORMES	Grebes

Sizes of birds: measurements are from beak to tail or beak to toe, whichever is the greater

Studies of fossils and comparative anatomy show that birds are descended from reptiles. The earliest bird—still almost a reptile in its general construction—probably appeared about 140 million years ago. Birds' feathers are derived from reptilian scales, their forelimbs are modified into wings, and their light, delicate bones with air-filled cavities are well adapted to flight. Like mammals, birds have a constant body temperature—averaging 3°C more than that of mammals—and a four-chambered heart. In most birds the breastbone has a keel-like projection of bone to which the powerful wing muscles are attached; there are no teeth in the horny beak.

The class Aves was formerly divided into two sub-classes—the ratites (running birds, with very small wings and an unkeeled breastbone) and the flying birds. Now, however, it is divided only into 27 orders of equal status, of which one—Passeriformes—contains more than half of the known bird species.

ORDER APTERYGIFORMES

There is one family:

FAMILY APTERYGIDAE

Kiwis; 3 species

These flightless New Zealand birds—surviving relatives of the extinct New Zealand moas—have short, muscular legs and strong claws. Their hair-like feathers hide their stubby wings and they lack tails. They inhabit forested areas, remaining hidden by day. At night they probe for invertebrates with their long bills. The females are larger than males. Example:

Large grey kiwi *Apteryx haasti*: found only in the South Island. Like the other two species it is a slow breeder, usually laying only one egg. Incubation, which takes about 11 weeks, is often carried out by the male

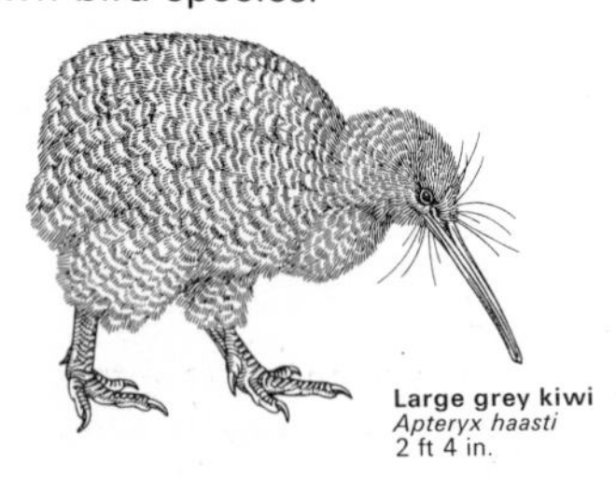

Large grey kiwi
Apteryx haasti
2 ft 4 in.

ORDER STRUTHIONIFORMES

There is one family:

FAMILY STRUTHIONIDAE

There is one species:

Ostrich *Struthio camelus*: the ostrich is the largest living bird. Its weight, small wings and inadequate wing muscles combine to make it flightless. It is a swift runner. There are only two toes on each foot. Ostriches live in bands of 10–50, mainly in southern and eastern Africa, but are also found in the Sahara

Ostrich
Struthio camelus
Up to 7 ft

ORDER RHEIFORMES

There is one family:

FAMILY RHEIDAE

Rheas; 2 species

The largest birds in the New World, rheas live in flocks on the pampas. The head, neck and thighs are feathered, but they have no tail plumes. Example:

Common rhea or **South American ostrich** *Rhea americana*: feeds on vegetable matter or insects

Common rhea or **South American ostrich**
Rhea americana
Up to 5 ft 6 in.

ORDER CASUARIIFORMES

Cassowaries and emu

These heavily built, flightless birds have coarse plumage, but the head and neck are virtually featherless. The young are longitudinally striped. There are two families:

FAMILY CASUARIIDAE

Cassowaries; 3 species

Found in forests from New Guinea to northern Australia, the cassowaries have a large bony crest on the forehead, possibly used to fend off obstructions as they run through the undergrowth, and a spike-like inner toe. The skin of the head and the neck is blue or purple. Example:

Australian cassowary *Casuarius casuarius*: lives in Australia

FAMILY DROMAIIDAE

There is one species:

Emu *Dromaius novaehollandiae*: found on the Australian plains. It has no crest, and the head and neck are feathered except for a blue spot on each side. It has brown and yellow stripes as a chick and deep brown plumage when adult

Australian cassowary
Casuarius casuarius
4 ft 6 in.–5 ft

Emu
Dromaius novaehollandiae
Over 6 ft

ORDER TINAMIFORMES

There is one family:

FAMILY TINAMIDAE

Tinamous; 50 species

Tinamous, which are brown or grey birds (often barred and mottled), have short tails. They can fly. Example:

Little tinamou *Crypturellus soui*: found in forests and savanna from southern Mexico to southern Brazil

Little tinamou
Crypturellus soui
11 in.

ORDER PODICIPEDIFORMES

There is one family:

FAMILY PODICIPEDIDAE

Grebes; 21 species

The weak-flying grebes have long, thin necks and pointed bills. The feet, set far back on the body, have stiff horny flaps on the toes which increase the surface area for swimming. Example:

Great crested grebe *Podiceps cristatus*: found in fresh waters in the Old World. It has two stiff tufts of black feathers on its head

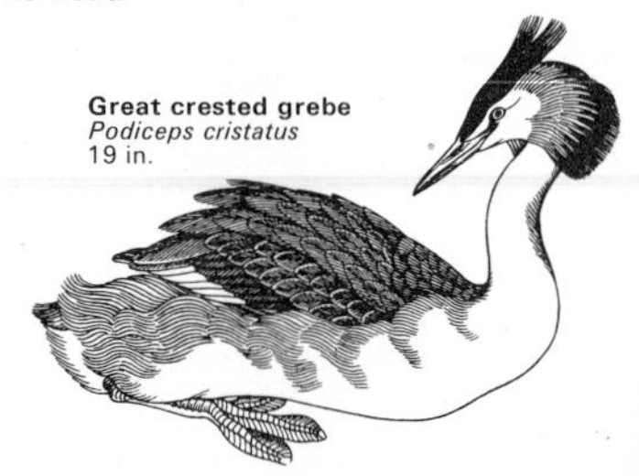

Great crested grebe
Podiceps cristatus
19 in.

PHYLUM CHORDATA	Animals with notochords
SUB-PHYLUM VERTEBRATA	Animals with backbones
CLASS AVES	Birds
ORDER GAVIIFORMES	Divers

ORDER SPHENISCIFORMES	Penguins
ORDER PROCELLARIIFORMES	Albatrosses, shearwaters and petrels
ORDER PELECANIFORMES	Pelicans and allies

ORDER GAVIIFORMES

There is one family:

FAMILY GAVIIDAE

Divers or loons; 5 species
These Arctic birds have legs encased in body skin down to the ankles, and webbed feet which are used for swimming. Their bodies are streamlined for diving. Example:
Great northern diver or **common loon** *Gavia immer*: it swims on fresh water in summer but seeks unfrozen salt water in winter

Great northern diver or **common loon**
Gavia immer
2–3 ft

ORDER SPHENISCIFORMES

There is one family:

FAMILY SPHENISCIDAE

Penguins; 18 species
These Southern Hemisphere birds have feet far back on the body and body skin covering the legs down to the ankles. They swim with their wings. Example:
Jackass or **black-footed penguin** *Spheniscus demersus*: breeds on South African shores. It is called 'jackass' because it brays rather like a donkey

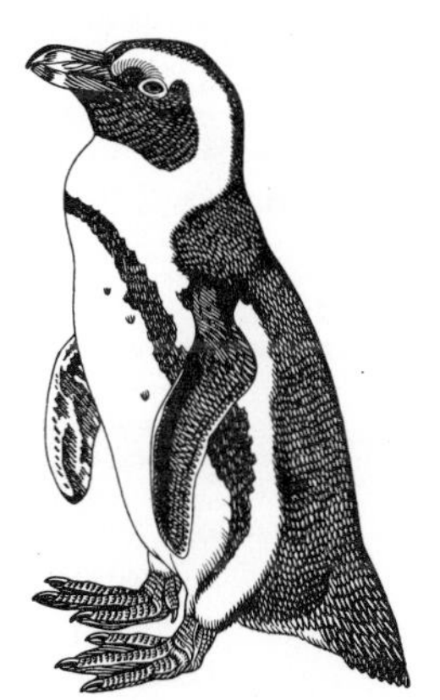

Jackass or **black-footed penguin**
Spheniscus demersus
18 in.

ORDER PROCELLARIIFORMES

Albatrosses, shearwaters and petrels
The oceanic birds of this order, characterised by long tubular nostrils opening out of their hooked bills, seldom come ashore except to breed. They discharge a clear yellow stomach oil when disturbed. This oil is also used to feed the young. These birds usually nest in a burrow in the ground. There are four families:

FAMILY DIOMEDEIDAE

Albatrosses; 13 species
These large, stout-bodied birds with long, narrow wings are superb gliders. Example:
Wandering albatross *Diomedea exulans*: lives in the southern oceans

FAMILY PROCELLARIIDAE

Shearwaters and fulmars; 53 species
This is a marine and highly migratory family of birds with slender bodies and webbed feet. They skim low over the water. Example:
Fulmar *Fulmarus glacialis*: found in the Northern Hemisphere

FAMILY HYDROBATIDAE

Storm petrels; 20 species
These small dark birds are named petrels after St Peter, because they lower their feet as they skim over the surface of the sea and appear to walk on it. They have short, broad wings, which they use to support their top-heavy bodies when running on land. Example:
Storm petrel *Hydrobates pelagicus*: breeds in dense colonies on islands off the coast of Europe and in the western Mediterranean

FAMILY PELECANOIDIDAE

Diving petrels; 5 species
These stout, short-billed birds dive for crustaceans and fish instead of taking them from the surface like storm petrels. Example:
Peruvian diving petrel *Pelecanoides garnotii*: found off the western coast of South America

ORDER PELECANIFORMES

Pelicans and allies
These are the only birds with all four toes webbed, but only the pelicans have a large pouch suspended from the bill. There are six families:

FAMILY PHAETHONTIDAE

Tropic birds; 3 species
The black-and-white tropic birds are found only in tropical seas, often hundreds of miles from land. Example:
White-tailed or **yellow-billed tropic bird** *Phaethon lepturus*: lives in the Atlantic, Indian and Pacific Oceans

FAMILY PELECANIDAE

Pelicans; 8 species
The pelican's large beak-pouch holds two or three times as much as its stomach, and is used as a scoop to catch fish. Pelicans breed on big lakes, and some go to the coast in winter. Example:
White pelican *Pelecanus onocrotalus*: found in Eurasia and Africa

FAMILY PHALACROCORACIDAE

Cormorants and shags; 30 species
These coastal birds, which have long bodies, necks and hooked beaks, hunt by diving for their underwater prey. They cannot fly long distances because, like the divers, their wings are short. Example:
Common cormorant *Phalacrocorax carbo*: found on coasts of northern Europe, Iceland, western Greenland, Africa, Asia, Australia and New Zealand

FAMILY ANHINGIDAE

Darters; 4 species
Darters, found in warm waters throughout the world, are like cormorants but have long, straight, pointed bills. They often swim partly submerged, with only their heads out of water. Example:
American anhinga *Anhinga anhinga*: found from southern U.S.A. to Argentina

FAMILY SULIDAE

Gannets and boobies; 9 species
These birds, which inhabit coastal waters and islands in tropical and temperate seas, have long, pointed wings, straight, sharp bills, long tails, and short, stout legs. They dive from a great height and chase fish under water. Example:
Masked booby *Sula dactylatra*: nests in colonies on cliffs in the tropics

FAMILY FREGATIDAE

Frigate-birds; 5 species
Their big wingspan enables frigate-birds to soar effortlessly for hours. They rarely enter the sea, and usually feed by making other birds disgorge their food. Example:
Magnificent frigate-bird *Fregata magnificens*: commonly found in the tropical waters of the south Atlantic, Pacific and Indian Oceans

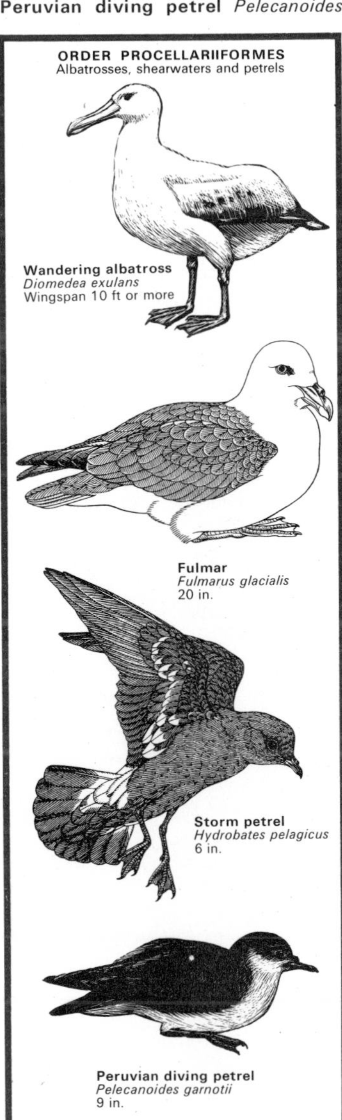

ORDER PROCELLARIIFORMES
Albatrosses, shearwaters and petrels

Wandering albatross
Diomedea exulans
Wingspan 10 ft or more

Fulmar
Fulmarus glacialis
20 in.

Storm petrel
Hydrobates pelagicus
6 in.

Peruvian diving petrel
Pelecanoides garnotii
9 in.

ORDER PELECANIFORMES
Pelicans and allies

White-tailed or **yellow-billed tropic bird**
Phaethon lepturus
2 ft 8 in.

American anhinga
Anhinga anhinga
3 ft

White pelican
Pelecanus onocrotalus
5 ft 6 in.

Masked booby
Sula dactylatra
2 ft 3 in.

Magnificent frigate bird
Fregata magnificens
Wingspan 7 ft

Common cormorant
Phalacrocorax carbo
3 ft 4 in.

PHYLUM CHORDATA	Animals with notochords
SUB-PHYLUM VERTEBRATA	Animals with backbones
CLASS AVES	Birds
ORDER CICONIIFORMES	Herons, storks and flamingoes
ORDER ANSERIFORMES	Screamers and ducks
ORDER FALCONIFORMES	Eagles, hawks and vultures

ORDER CICONIIFORMES

Herons, storks and flamingoes
Most birds in this group have long, featherless legs adapted for wading, a long bill, broad, rounded wings, short tails and four long, spreading toes on each foot. They feed on fish, aquatic animals and insects. There are seven families:

FAMILY ARDEIDAE

Herons; 64 species
The heron's neck is permanently S-shaped because the development of the vertebrae is uneven. The middle toe has a serrated claw. Example:
Purple heron *Ardea purpurea*: found in freshwater marshes and on river banks in the Old World. It nests in colonies

FAMILY COCHLEARIIDAE

There is one species:
Boat-billed heron *Cochlearius cochlearius*: lives in the mangroves of Central and South America. It has a broad, scoop-like bill and a combed claw

FAMILY BALAENICIPITIDAE

There is one species:
Shoebill or **whale-headed stork** *Balaeniceps rex*: lives in the papyrus swamps of the White Nile. It has a combed middle claw and a wide, 8 in. long beak. It flies with its neck folded

FAMILY SCOPIDAE

There is one species:
Hammerkop *Scopus umbretta*: flies with neck extended like a stork, but possesses heron-like vocal organs. It has serrated claws and a fourth toe level with the other toes. It lives in Africa

FAMILY CICONIIDAE

Storks; 17 species
Storks do not have a serrated middle claw. Their short toes are partly webbed at the base, and the hind toe is elevated above the other three. Example:
White stork *Ciconia ciconia*: nests in Europe and eastern Asia; the European population winters in South Africa and the Middle East

FAMILY THRESKIORNITHIDAE

Ibises and spoonbills; 32 species
These birds are like storks, but the hind toe is only slightly elevated, and the middle claw only slightly serrated. Example:
Sacred ibis *Threskiornis aethiopica*: widespread in Africa, it has a large body, short legs and a thin, down-curved bill

FAMILY PHOENICOPTERIDAE

Flamingoes; 4 species
Flamingoes fly with their necks straight, their legs trailing behind, and honk like geese during flight. The hind toe is elevated or absent, and the others are webbed. These birds breed in tropical brackish waters. Example:
Greater flamingo *Phoenicopterus ruber*: found in the Americas, Africa, Europe and western Asia

ORDER ANSERIFORMES

Screamers and ducks
These full-bodied waterfowl have a long neck and a feathered oil gland situated near the base of the tail. The oil, transferred to the feathers by the bill, waterproofs the body. There are two families:

FAMILY ANHIMIDAE

Screamers; 3 species
These are rather long-legged South American waders with a short, curved bill, little webbing on the toes, and two sharp spurs on the front edge of each wing. They have a harsh, resounding cry. Example:
Horned screamer *Anhima cornuta*: lives in the flooded forests and marshes of tropical South America

FAMILY ANATIDAE

Swans, geese, ducks; 145 species
These are gregarious water birds, with short legs, webbed front toes and broad bills. Most of them dive for their food. Example:
Canada goose *Branta canadensis*: breeds on lake shores and marshes in Canada and Alaska and migrate in winter to coastal and southern states of the U.S.A.

ORDER FALCONIFORMES

Eagles, hawks and vultures
These birds of prey, which are active during the day, have sharp, down-hooked bills with a waxy membrane across the base, through which the nostrils open. They lay small clutches of eggs and incubation is lengthy. There are five families:

FAMILY CATHARTIDAE

American vultures and condors; 6 species
The toes of these birds are weak and adapted for walking and running, not clutching; the three front toes have rudimentary webbing. Their bills are also weak and unable to tear most flesh until it is partly decayed. Example:
King vulture *Sarcorhamphus papa*: found from southern Mexico to the tropical forests of northern Argentina. It has a bare neck and a wattle on its beak

ORDER FALCONIFORMES
Eagles, hawks and vultures

King vulture *Sarcorhamphus papa* Wingspan 6 ft

Osprey *Pandion haliaetus* Up to 24 in.

Secretary bird *Sagittarius serpentarius* 4 ft

Peregrine falcon *Falco peregrinus* Up to 20 in.

African fish eagle *Haliaeëtus vocifer* 2 ft 6 in.

FAMILY SAGITTARIIDAE

There is one species:
Secretary bird *Sagittarius serpentarius*: found in sparsely wooded grasslands or veldts in Africa. It has a long crest and long legs. It can fly, but usually runs. It eats snakes and other reptiles

FAMILY ACCIPITRIDAE

Eagles, hawks and Old World vultures; 205 species
These birds have broad wings, usually rounded at the tip, and strong claws. Unlike falcons, they have no notch or 'tooth' on the bill. Examples:
Griffon vulture *Gyps fulvus* (up to 3 ft 5 in.): a carrion-eater, found in the mountains of southern Europe, south-west Asia and Africa. It can draw its neck into its neck ruff
Goshawk *Accipiter gentilis* (24 in.): found in Eurasia and North America, nesting in clefts of branches. It strikes and pursues its victim, whereas most hawks disable prey in passing and return for it
African fish eagle *Haliaeëtus vocifer*: common on the banks of African rivers and lakes. It has a powerful bill and legs

FAMILY PANDIONIDAE

There is one species:
Osprey *Pandion haliaetus*: widely distributed near water, where it catches fish. It has broad, pointed wings and four toes of equal length, the outer one being reversible

FAMILY FALCONIDAE

Falcons; 58 species
These birds have long pointed wings, bare ankles and feet, and a notch or 'tooth' on the upper part of the bill. They do not make nests but breed on the ground, on ledges or in deserted nests. Example:
Peregrine falcon *Falco peregrinus*: practically worldwide in coastal areas

ORDER GALLIFORMES

Game birds and hoatzin
Most of this group are ground-living birds with short, turned-down bills and long, heavy feet, with a short fourth toe behind and short, rounded wings. There are seven families:

FAMILY MEGAPODIDAE

Megapodes; 12 species
Found from Australia to Malaya, the megapodes (from the Greek for 'large feet') rarely fly. They build enormous nests in which their eggs are incubated by the heat of rotting vegetation, stored warmth from the sun or volcanic heat. The fourth toe is almost level with the others. Example:
Mallee fowl *Leipoa ocellata*: found in inland southern Australia. It lays its eggs in large mounds of leaf mould and covers them with sand. The male regulates the temperature of the mound by adding or removing sand

FAMILY CRACIDAE

Curassows; 43 species
Curassows nest in trees but feed mainly on the ground. The fourth toe is level with the others. Curassows have shaggy, permanently erect crests and the male has a brightly coloured bill. Example:
Great curassow *Crax rubra*: found in tropical forests from Mexico to Central America

FAMILY TETRAONIDAE

Grouse; 18 species
The ankles of these birds are at least partly feathered, and most grouse grow fringes on their toes in winter. The fourth toe is elevated. The nostrils are feathered and there is often a bright, bare eye-patch. Example:
Capercaillie *Tetrao urogallus*: found in Eurasian coniferous forests. The male displays its tail in the breeding season

FAMILY PHASIANIDAE

Fowl; 165 species
Most fowl are heavily built ground-living birds, with feathered nostrils, naked feet and spurs on the back of the legs. They cannot fly for long. Examples:
Partridge *Perdix perdix* (12–18 in.): lives in dunes, heaths and grassland in Europe and western Asia. It nests in a straw-lined hollow in the ground
Common or **ringed pheasant** *Phasianus colchicus*: a native of central Asia, introduced to Europe by the Romans
Indian jungle fowl *Gallus gallus*: lives in Asian tropical forests, from sea level to 5000 ft. It is the ancestor of all domestic breeds and was domesticated in India by 3200 BC

FAMILY NUMIDIDAE

Guinea fowl; 10 species
These African game birds are generally found in flocks in bushy grasslands and open forests. They have a bare head and neck, dark feathers spangled with white, and rudimentary spurs. Example:
Vulturine or **long-tailed guinea fowl** *Acryllium vulturinum*: lives in East Africa

FAMILY MELEAGRIDIDAE

Turkeys; 2 species
Found throughout the world as domestic birds and occasionally in the wild in North and Central America, turkeys have spurs, and rudimentary webs between the toes. Their heads and necks are naked; the males have long throat pouches and both sexes have nose pouches. Example:
Common turkey *Meleagris gallopavo*: lives in open woodland and forest clearings in southern North America

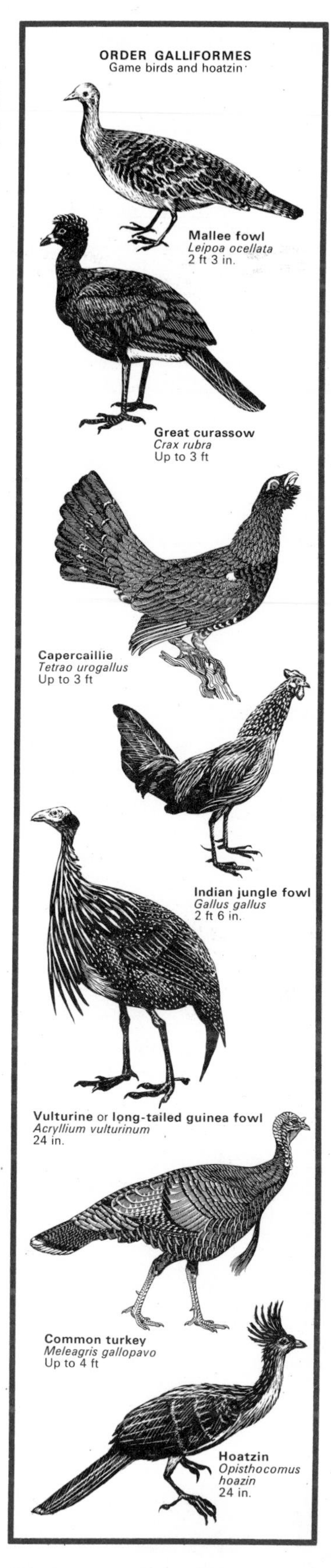

ORDER GALLIFORMES
Game birds and hoatzin

Mallee fowl *Leipoa ocellata* 2 ft 3 in.

Great curassow *Crax rubra* Up to 3 ft

Capercaillie *Tetrao urogallus* Up to 3 ft

Indian jungle fowl *Gallus gallus* 2 ft 6 in.

Vulturine or **long-tailed guinea fowl** *Acryllium vulturinum* 24 in.

Common turkey *Meleagris gallopavo* Up to 4 ft

Hoatzin *Opisthocomus hoazin* 24 in.

FAMILY OPISTHOCOMIDAE

There is one species:
Hoatzin *Opisthocomus hoazin*: lives beside rivers in South American tropical forest. It is a brown, pheasant-like bird with a long loose crest and a huge crop. The chicks have two well-developed claws at the tip of each wing with which they creep along branches

Birds

SUB-PHYLUM VERTEBRATA	Animals with backbones
CLASS AVES	Birds
ORDER GRUIFORMES	Cranes and allies
ORDER CHARADRIIFORMES	Waders, gulls and auks

ORDER GRUIFORMES

Cranes and allies
Members of this order have long necks, lack webs on their feet, and usually have long legs. There are 11 families:

FAMILY MESITORNITHIDAE

Mesites; 3 species
These are rather thrush-like birds from Madagascar which have functional wings but do not fly. They have five pairs of powder-down feather patches—disintegrating feather material used for cleaning the feathers. Example:
Brown mesite *Mesoenas unicolor*: common in the rain forest of eastern Madagascar. It nests in a platform of sticks about 3 ft above the ground

FAMILY TURNICIDAE

Button or bustard quails; 14 species
Button quails are secretive, ground-living birds found in Old World grasslands. Example:
Barred bustard quail *Turnix suscitator*: found in southern Asia. It seldom flies but can run fast

FAMILY GRUIDAE

Cranes; 15 species
Cranes are gregarious birds found in open marshy land in all continents except South America and Antarctica. They have a partly bare head and elevated hind toes. Their cry is resonant and they also clack their bills like storks. Cranes migrate in V-formation, flying with their necks straight out. They dance during courtship. Example:
Manchurian or **Japanese crane** *Grus japonensis*: found in marshes in Manchuria, Korea, eastern China and Japan

FAMILY ARAMIDAE

There is one species:
Limpkin *Aramus guarauna*: found in marshes from Florida to Argentina, it is related to both cranes and rails. It is a large, grey-brown bird whose long hind toes are level with the front ones

FAMILY PSOPHIDAE

Trumpeters; 3 species
Trumpeters have long legs and short bills. Example:
Grey-winged trumpeter *Psophia crepitans*: lives in humid tropical forest in north-eastern South America

FAMILY RALLIDAE

Rails, moorhens and coots; 132 species
These birds are often weak flyers, with vertically flattened bodies and long toes. Example:
Moorhen or **common gallinule** *Gallinula chloropus*: lives in marshes in temperate and tropical areas of the Americas, Africa and Eurasia

FAMILY HELIORNITHIDAE

Finfoots; 3 species
These are secretive, grebe-like birds with long bodies and bills. They are found in South America, Africa and south-east Asia. Example:
African finfoot *Podica senegalensis*: found in tropical streams. It hunts from low perches which are sometimes partly submerged

FAMILY RHYNOCHETIDAE

There is one species:
Kagu *Rhynochetos jubatus*: found in New Caledonia, it sleeps among rocks or under tree roots by day. It has a red bill and a big crest

FAMILY CARIAMIDAE

Seriamas; 2 species
These large South American birds have a crest, down-curved at the tip, at the base of the beak. Example:
Crested seriama *Cariama cristata*: found in open grasslands in Brazil and Paraguay

FAMILY EURYPYGIDAE

There is one species:
Sun bittern *Eurypyga helias*: a solitary wader with a long bill, which it uses to spear its prey. It is found in Central and South America

FAMILY OTIDIDAE

Bustards; 22 species
These powerful runners of the Old World grasslands can fly but usually do not; they are grey-brown, barred and spotted, and sometimes have a crest. They lay their eggs on the ground. Example:
Great bustard *Otis tarda*: lives on the plains of Eurasia and North Africa. It is one of the largest flying birds

ORDER CHARADRIIFORMES

Waders, auks and gulls
Most of this order are medium-sized waders or shore birds possessing a tufted oil gland. There are 16 families:

FAMILY JACANIDAE

Jacanas or lily trotters; 7 species
Found in the Old and New Worlds in tropical pools, jacanas have very long toes and claws which enable them to walk on water-lilies and other floating leaves. They have a frontal shield on the bill, and sharp, horny spurs on the wings. Example:
American jacana *Jacana spinosa*: found from Texas to Argentina

FAMILY ROSTRATULIDAE

Painted snipes; 2 species
These are long, straight-billed, green-brown birds found in southern Asia, Africa, South America and Australia. Example:
Painted snipe *Rostratula benghalensis*: lives in tropical and sub-tropical Africa, Madagascar, southern Asia and Australia

FAMILY HAEMATOPODIDAE

Oyster-catchers; 6 species
These noisy birds have long, blunt, flat bills which they use to open shellfish. Example:
European oyster-catcher *Haematopus ostralegus*: common along coasts

FAMILY CHARADRIIDAE

Plovers; 56 species
These plump birds have short bills, slightly swollen at the tip, and are found all over the world. They have bold black or brown markings on white. They migrate in flocks of thousands. Example:
Lapwing *Vanellus vanellus*: lives in temperate Eurasia and nests in the open. It is a noisy bird

FAMILY SCOLOPACIDAE

Sandpipers; 70 species
This is a group of drab-coloured, ground-dwelling waders with thin, straight or down-curved bills. Examples:
Common snipe *Gallinago gallinago* (11 in.): lives in marshes and meadows in Europe, northern Asia, Africa, the Americas
Common sandpiper *Tringa hypoleucos*: found on the banks of rivers and streams in Eurasia and North America

FAMILY RECURVIROSTRIDAE

Avocets and stilts; 7 species
The members of this widely distributed family of long-legged waders have slender legs and very long thin bills. Only the avocets have up-curved bills. Example:
Eurasian avocet *Recurvirostra avosetta*: breeds in Eurasia and Africa. It walks along, skimming the surface of water or mud with its up-curved bill in search of small invertebrates

FAMILY PHALAROPODIDAE

Phalaropes; 3 species
All the phalaropes have lobe-webbed feet and toes like grebes, and thin, straight bills. They nest in the Arctic tundra and winter in the Southern ,Hemisphere, especially in Argentina. Example:
Grey or **red phalarope** *Phalaropus fulicarius*: found from the Arctic to the southern oceans. It feeds on plankton

FAMILY DROMADIDAE

There is one species:
Crab plover *Dromas ardeola*: found on the coasts of the Indian Ocean and the Red Sea. It has a long, straight, pointed bill and partly webbed toes

PHYLUM CHORDATA	Animals with notochords
SUB-PHYLUM VERTEBRATA	Animals with backbones
CLASS AVES	Birds
ORDER CHARADRIIFORMES	Waders, gulls and auks
ORDER COLUMBIFORMES	Pigeons and sandgrouse
ORDER PSITTACIFORMES	Parrots

FAMILY BURHINIDAE

Stone curlews and thick knees; 9 species

All have swollen knee joints, short bills and large eyes. They are found in pebbly areas all over the world. Example:

Stone curlew *Burhinus oedicnemus*: found in Europe, south-west Asia and North Africa

FAMILY GLAREOLIDAE

Coursers and pratincoles; 16 species

These gregarious, insect-eating, running birds, with down-curved bills, are found in sandy areas of the Old World. They also feed on fish and seeds. Example:

Common pratincole *Glareola pratincola*: ranges over southern Europe, Africa and southern Asia

FAMILY THINOCORIDAE

Seedsnipes; 4 species

Seedsnipes are plump, short-legged birds, with stout, sparrow-like bills and long wings. They are found in tundra in southern South America and in the Andes northwards to the Equator. Example:

D'Orbigny's seedsnipe *Thinocorus orbignyianus*: feeds on seeds, tender shoots and leaves

FAMILY CHIONIDIDAE

Sheathbills or paddies; 2 species

These bold scavengers, found on islands near the Antarctic and some mainland coasts, have a horny, saddle-like sheath over the base of the upper bill. They feed on gulls' eggs and chicks. Example:

Sheathbill *Chionis alba*: lives on islands off Antarctic coasts

FAMILY STERCORARIIDAE

Skuas; 4 species

Skuas are strong flyers, living mainly in open waters. They breed in the Arctic and Antarctic, and winter in the middle latitudes. A horny protuberance on the base of the upper bill, through which the nostrils open, distinguishes them from gulls. They harass seabirds, forcing them to disgorge their food. Example:

Arctic skua *Stercorarius parasiticus*: found on coasts and islands through the Arctic and in Scandinavia, Nova Scotia and northern Scotland

FAMILY LARIDAE

Gulls and terns; 82 species

Gulls have no fleshy protuberance on their bills and do not migrate as far as the skuas. Terns are smaller and less plump than gulls, with narrower wings and thin, sharp bills. Example:

Greater black-backed gull *Larus marinus*: found on the Atlantic coasts of Europe and North America

FAMILY RYNCHOPIDAE

Skimmers; 3 species

Skimmers catch fish by flying with the longer, lower half of the bill just cutting the surface of the water. The sharp edge of the bill fits into a groove in the upper half of the bill. They are found on Atlantic coasts and by African and southern Asian rivers. Example:

Black skimmer *Rynchops nigra*: found from New Jersey to Argentina

FAMILY ALCIDAE

Auks; 22 species

Found in Europe, northern Asia and North America, these short-winged birds, with heavy bodies and legs placed far back, are the Northern Hemisphere's equivalent of penguins. They dive, swim with their wings, and fly. Example:

Razorbill *Alca torda*: found around North Atlantic coasts, it breeds in flocks on cliffs and islands

ORDER COLUMBIFORMES

Pigeons and sandgrouse

These are thickly feathered land birds, similar to the waders and gulls in palate and wing structure. They are vegetarian and, unlike other birds, they can swallow water without raising their heads. There are two families:

FAMILY PTEROCLIDAE

Sandgrouse; 16 species

Found in the tropics and sub-tropics of the Old World in open, sandy country; the sandgrouse have short, pointed bills without any protuberances, and legs which are feathered to the toes. Example:

Pallas's sandgrouse *Syrrhaptes paradoxus*: found in central Asia

FAMILY COLUMBIDAE

Pigeons; 289 species

The members of this worldwide family have short necks, small heads, and slender bills with a protuberance at the base. Two eggs are laid in a nest consisting of a flimsy stick platform; the male incubates by day, the female by night. The young are fed on 'pigeon's milk', a liquid from the lining of the crop. Example:

Rock dove *Columba livia*: the ancestor of the domestic pigeon, found in Europe, India, west and central Asia, and north and western Africa. It nests on cliffs on the coast or on mountains

ORDER PSITTACIFORMES

There is one family:

FAMILY PSITTACIDAE

Parrots, parakeets, cockatoos, macaws and lories; 315 species

These mainly tropical and Southern Hemisphere birds have big heads, short necks, strong, down-curved upper bills with a broad protuberance at the base, and feet with two toes in front and two behind. They are long-lived birds, some of them living 80 years. Examples:

African grey parrot *Psittacus erithacus*: found in African tropical forest. It is the finest talking bird when trained

African grey parrot
Psittacus erithacus
13 in.

CLASSIFICATION

Birds

PHYLUM CHORDATA	Animals with notochords
SUB-PHYLUM VERTEBRATA	Animals with backbones
CLASS AVES	Birds
ORDER CUCULIFORMES	Cuckoos and turacos
ORDER STRIGIFORMES	Owls
ORDER CAPRIMULGIFORMES	Frogmouths and nightjars
ORDER APODIFORMES	Swifts and hummingbirds

ORDER CUCULIFORMES

Cuckoos and turacos
Members of this order are closely related to the parrots, with similar feet. They have no protuberance or hook on the upper bill. There are two families:

FAMILY MUSOPHAGIDAE

Turacos and plantain eaters; 20 species
These birds are often brilliantly coloured with long tails, high crests and fourth toes that can be turned forwards. They feed on fruit and insects. Example:
Knysa turaco *Tauraco corythaix*: found in South African forests

FAMILY CUCULIDAE

Cuckoos; 127 species
Cuckoos are slender birds with long tails, down-curved bills and pointed wings, found in all the warmer regions of the world. Example:
Common cuckoo *Cuculus canorus*: found in Eurasia and Africa. Only the male cries 'cuckoo'

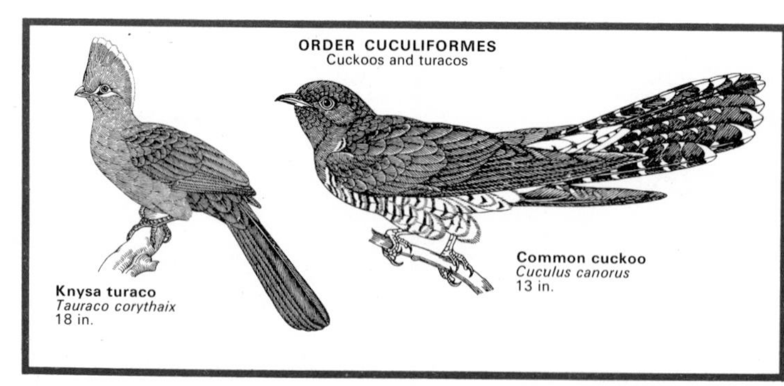

ORDER STRIGIFORMES

Owls
The members of this worldwide order—the owls—have short mobile necks, and commonly have soft, fluffy plumage which silences their flight. Most owls are nocturnal. There are two families:

FAMILY TYTONIDAE

Barn owls; 10 species
The barn owls have heart-shaped faces, fully feathered long legs, and a serrated comb on the middle claw. They nest in hollow trees and buildings and detect prey largely by sound. Example:
Common barn owl *Tyto alba*: has almost worldwide distribution

FAMILY STRIGIDAE

Typical owls; 120 species
These round-faced birds, with huge eyes, bare feet and no serrated comb, hunt by sight as well as by sound. They nest in hollow trees, on cliff edges and in ground burrows. Example:
Great eagle owl *Bubo bubo*: found in woods of Europe, Asia and North Africa

ORDER CAPRIMULGIFORMES

Frogmouths and nightjars
These birds, with long pointed wings, small feet and huge gaping mouths, are active at dusk or night, feeding mainly on insects, which are usually caught on the wing. There are five families:

FAMILY STEATORNITHIDAE

There is one species:
Oilbird *Steatornis caripenses*: found in caves in northern South America, this bird is a fruit-eater, with a stout, hooked bill. In the dark caves where it roosts, it navigates by echo-location, but emitting sounds at lower pitches that are audible to humans

FAMILY PODARGIDAE

Frogmouths; 12 species
Found from Australia to Malaya, the frogmouths are nocturnal birds with large, flat, horny, triangular and sharply hooked bills. They prey on mice as well as on insects. They have short wings and silky plumage. Example:
Tawny frogmouth *Podargus strigoides*: lives in forests in Australia and Tasmania

FAMILY NYCTIBIIDAE

Potoos or wood-nightjars; 5 species
Found in Central and South America, the potoos sit bolt upright on tree stumps, resembling a broken branch. Example:
Common potoo *Nyctibius griseus*: has very short legs and large eyes

FAMILY AEGOTHELIDAE

Owlet frogmouths; 6 species
These birds, which are like tiny, long-tailed owls, do not adopt the broken-branch camouflage of the potoos. They are found in Australia and New Guinea. Example:
Rufous owlet frogmouth *Aegotheles insignis*: found in New Guinea

FAMILY CAPRIMULGIDAE

Nightjars; 70 species
These birds have a loud monotonous call. They fly quietly with slow wingbeats, and are found all over the world except in the Arctic and Antarctic. Most species are active at dusk or night. Example:
Whip poor-will *Caprimulgus vociferus*: found in North and Central America

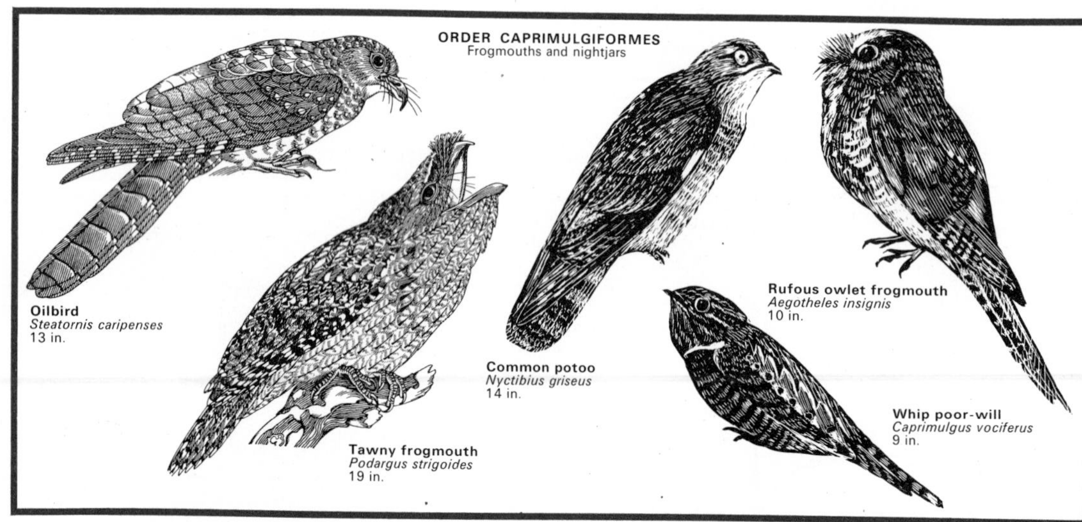

ORDER APODIFORMES

Swifts and humming birds
These are fast-flying, short-legged and weak-footed birds of the tropics and sub-tropics. There are three families:

FAMILY APODIDAE

Swifts; 65 species
Swifts, some flying between 150 and 200 mph, catch insects on the wing, high in the air. They fly faster, straighter and less erratically than the unrelated swallows. Their rapid wing-beats alternate with gliding, and they steer with their wings as their tails are too short. Example:
White-rumped swift *Apus caffer*: lives in Africa

FAMILY HEMIPROCNIDAE

Crested swifts; 3 species
These swifts, with their long, forked tails, softer plumage and erectile crests, are not as highly specialised for flight as other swifts. They perch on trees. Example:
Indian crested swift *Hemiprocne coronata*: lives near tropical forest verges

FAMILY TROCHILIDAE

Hummingbirds; 319 species
These are tiny American birds, with slender, pointed bills and tubular, fringe-tipped tongues projecting beyond their beaks. Their wings hum in flight; they never soar, but they can hover. Example:
Ruby-throated hummingbird *Archilochus colubris*: lives in jungles and tropical mountains in Central America and eastern North America

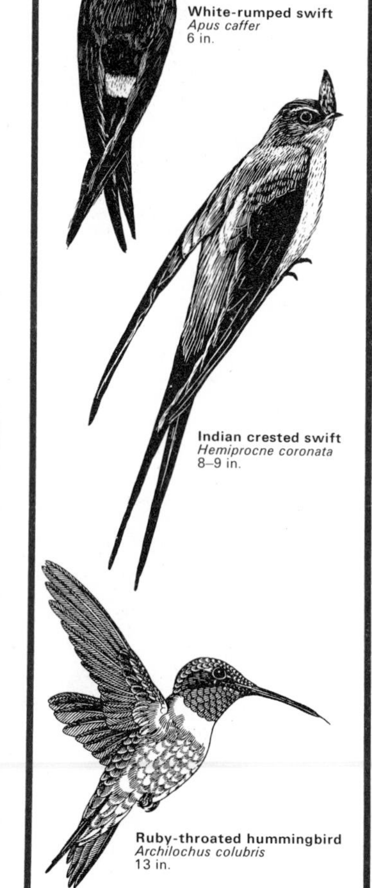

PHYLUM CHORDATA	Animals with notochords
SUB-PHYLUM VERTEBRATA	Animals with backbones
CLASS AVES	Birds
ORDER TROGONIFORMES	Trogons
ORDER COLIIFORMES	Colies
ORDER CORACIIFORMES	Kingfishers, hornbills and allies

ORDER TROGONIFORMES

There is one family:

FAMILY TROGONIDAE

Trogons; 35 species

These brightly coloured, sedentary birds are found in all tropical forests. The first and second toes turn backwards, and they have weak legs, feathered ankles, short wings and a long square tail. Trogons nest in tree holes. Example: **Quetzal** *Pharomachrus mocinno*: found in forests in Central America

Quetzal
Pharomachrus mocinno
4 ft

ORDER CORACIIFORMES

Kingfishers, hornbills and allies

These carnivorous birds are found all over the world. Two or three of their front toes are partly fused. There are eight families:

FAMILY ALCEDINIDAE

Kingfishers and kookaburras; 80 species

These are thick-set birds, with short, thick necks, short tails, big heads (often crested) and long sharp beaks. Example: **Common kingfisher** *Alcedo atthis*: found by Old World streams and lakes, feeding on fish

FAMILY TODIDAE

Todies; 5 species

Todies are very small West Indian birds with finely serrated flattened bills, green backs and red breasts. They nest in horizontal burrows up to 12 in. long, which they excavate in earth or sand with their bills. They catch insects by swooping down suddenly like kingfishers. Example: **Jamaican tody** *Todus todus*: found near forest verges and in bushy areas

FAMILY MOMOTIDAE

Motmots; 8 species

Quiet birds of Central and South American tropical forests, the motmots have soft, brightly coloured feathers and long tails. They hop clumsily. Example: **Blue-crowned motmot** *Momotus momota*: like the other species of motmots, it nests in burrows

FAMILY MEROPIDAE

Bee-eaters; 24 species

The Old World bee-eaters are colourful, slender birds with long, down-curved beaks and long, slender tail feathers. They eat bees and locusts. Example: **Common bee-eater** *Merops apiaster*: found in Europe, Asia and Africa

FAMILY CORACIIDAE

Rollers; 11 species

These birds of the Old World tropics have stout bills, big heads and long tails. Some species display with acrobatic flights involving rolls, twists and dives. They eat insects, frogs, mice and small lizards. They hop clumsily. Example: **Abyssinian roller** *Coracias abyssinica*: found in dry areas from south-west Arabia westwards to Senegal

FAMILY UPUPIDAE

There is one species: **Hoopoe** *Upupa epops*: found in open country in Eurasia and Africa. It has a long, curved, pointed bill and a crest. It feeds on the ground, nests in tree cavities—often unlined—and never removes feces or food from the nest. The female has a gland at the base of her tail which emits an offensive smell when she is brooding

FAMILY PHOENICULIDAE

Wood hoopoes; 16 species

These birds, which are found only in Africa, are slimmer in build than the hoopoe, and have no crest. They are tree-loving birds and are rarely seen on the ground. The female has a scent gland. Example: **Senegal wood hoopoe** *Phoeniculus senegalensis*: found in Africa

FAMILY BUCEROTIDAE

Hornbills; 45 species

These short-legged, black-and-white birds of the Old World tropical forests have huge, down-curved, serrated bills, usually with a horny protuberance on top. The bill is often highly coloured. When incubating her eggs, the female is walled into a tree-hole nest, leaving only a small opening through which the male can pass food to her. The female spends 30–50 days in the hole, and moults during this period. Example: **Great Indian hornbill** *Buceros bicornis*: lives in India, Malaya and Indonesia

ORDER COLIIFORMES

There is one family:

FAMILY COLIIDAE

Colies or mousebirds; 6 species

These gregarious African birds are acrobatic and often hang upside-down. They have a slender, prominent crest, a long thin tail and reversible first toes. Example: **Bar-breasted coly** or **speckled mousebird** *Colius striatus*: lives in Africa south of the Sahara

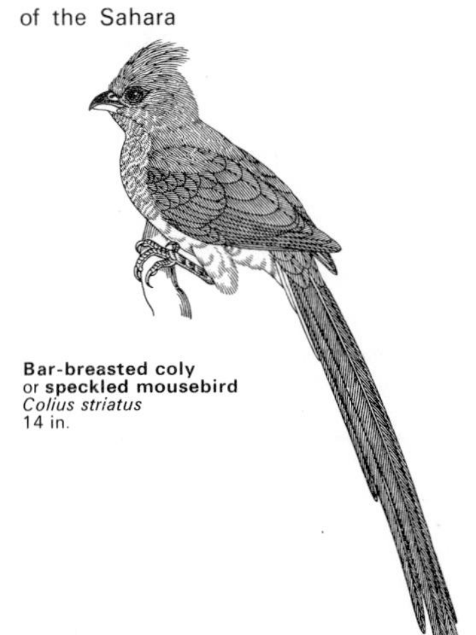

Bar-breasted coly
or speckled mousebird
Colius striatus
14 in.

CLASSIFICATION

Birds

PHYLUM CHORDATA	Animals with notochords
SUB-PHYLUM VERTEBRATA	Animals with backbones
CLASS AVES	Birds
ORDER PICIFORMES	Woodpeckers, barbets and toucans
ORDER PASSERIFORMES	Passerines

ORDER PICIFORMES

Woodpeckers, barbets and toucans
This is a group of tree-dwelling, usually solitary birds with two toes pointing forwards and two backwards. In some species the outer hind toe is lacking. There are six families:

FAMILY CAPITONIDAE
Barbets; 76 species
Found all over the world in tropical forests, these plump, gaudy birds have big, heavy bills and short wings. Example: **Black-spotted barbet** *Capito niger*: ranges from Panama to Brazil

FAMILY INDICATORIDAE
Honey-guides; 12 species
These dull-coloured relatives of the barbets feed on the wax of honeycombs. They lead honey-eating animals to bees' nests, and after the nest has been plundered the birds eat the wax. Example: **Greater honey-guide** *Indicator indicator*: widely distributed in tropical and southern Africa

FAMILY GALBULIDAE
Jacamars; 15 species
A family of Central and South American forest birds with tapering bodies, long, thin bills, and gaudy, long tails. Example: **Paradise jacamar** *Galbula dea*: found in northern South America

FAMILY BUCCONIDAE
Puffbirds; 30 species
These Central and South American birds are heavily built with big heads, flattened bills, and dark plumage. Example: **Collared puffbird** *Bucco capensis*: an inhabitant of South America

FAMILY RAMPHASTIDAE
Toucans; 37 species
These fruit-eaters, with brightly coloured, slightly down-curved bills, live in American tropical forests. Example: **Toco toucan** *Ramphastos toco*: found in South America

FAMILY PICIDAE
Woodpeckers; 230 species
The birds of this worldwide family have long, straight bills and tails, and strong front toes with sharp claws. They chip through the bark of trees with their bills to reach the insects underneath. Example: **Green woodpecker** *Picus viridis*: found in deciduous woodlands in Europe and western Asia

ORDER PASSERIFORMES

Passerines
This worldwide order of perching birds contains more than half of the known bird species. All have three, similar, unwebbed front toes and a hind toe which is highly developed but not reversible. Their young are born naked and helpless. There are 56 families listed here. However, they have evolved comparatively recently and are not well defined. Some authorities would divide the order into fewer families and some into more

FAMILY EURYLAIMIDAE
Broadbills; 14 species
Broadbills are brightly coloured forest birds of the Old World tropics. They have big heads and partly joined front toes. Example: **Dusky broadbill** *Corydon sumatranus*: found in Sumatra

FAMILY DENDROCOLAPTIDAE
Woodcreepers; 50 species
This is a family of New World tropical forest birds with partly joined front toes and vertically flattened bills. Example: **Barred woodcreeper** *Dendrocolaptes certhia*: found in the lower and middle layers of forests

FAMILY FURNARIIDAE
Ovenbirds; 221 species
These Central and South American birds are very similar to the woodcreepers. They build intricate, oven-shaped clay nests. Some species live on the ground and nest in burrows. Example: **Rufous ovenbird** *Furnarius rufus*: found in wooded areas of grasslands in South America

FAMILY FORMICARIIDAE
Antbirds; 223 species
Antbirds are similar to ovenbirds, but their beaks are hooked at the tip and they build simpler nests. They are confined to Central and South America. Example: **Scale-breasted ant pitta** *Grallaria excelsa* (9 in.): found in the high Andes of northern South America
Black-faced ant-thrush *Formicarius analis*: lives in South America in the undergrowth of forests and in scrub. It runs rather than flies when disturbed

FAMILY CONOPOPHAGIDAE
Ant pipits; 11 species
These small, stocky birds, with broad bills, are found on the floor of the Amazonian rain forests. Example: **Black-breasted gnat-eater** *Conopophaga melanogaster*: found in Brazil and Bolivia. The male has a black crown and prominent white brows

FAMILY RHINOCRYPTIDAE
Tapaculos; 30 species
These are ground-living birds, and fly very little. They have erect tails, long, strong legs and weak wings. They live in scrub or mountain forests in Central and South America. Example: **Great-footed turco** *Pteroptochus megapodius*: lives in northern and central Chile in hills and mountains at heights of up to 8000 ft

PHYLUM CHORDATA	Animals with notochords
SUB-PHYLUM VERTEBRATA	Animals with backbones
CLASS AVES	Birds
ORDER PASSERIFORMES	Passerines

FAMILY COTINGIDAE

Cotingas; 90 species

These solitary birds have a wide range of ornamentation and many have bare patches or wattles on their heads. They are found in forests from Argentina to Texas. Example:

Umbrella bird *Cephalopterus ornatus*: found high in the forest trees in Costa Rica and Brazil. A large, tubular, fleshy appendage hangs from its chest

FAMILY PIPRIDAE

Manakins; 59 species

These are brightly coloured, tiny birds that feed mainly on small fruits, plucked on the wing. The males perform elaborate courtship rites on special display grounds. Example:

Golden-headed manakin *Pipra erythrocephala*: like the rest of the family, it is confined to South American forests

FAMILY TYRANNIDAE

Tyrant flycatchers; 365 species

Related to the cotingas and manakins, tyrant flycatchers hunt in the open, capturing insects in short, speedy bursts of flight. Their crown feathers stand erect, and the birds are found throughout the Americas up to the timberline. Example:

Eastern kingbird *Tyrannus tyrannus*: found in North America, this bird has a drab coloured plumage on its upper parts and a white-tipped tail

FAMILY PHYTOTOMIDAE

Plantcutters; 3 species

These plump, finch-like birds with short, saw-toothed bills are found on the lower slopes of the Andes. Example:

Reddish plantcutter *Phytotoma rutila*: common in open forest and bush grasslands in Argentina

FAMILY OXYRUNCIDAE

There is one species:

Sharpbill *Oxyruncus cristatus*: this bird, which has a sharp beak with a feathery rim at the base, has no close relatives and is confined to the forests of Central and South America

FAMILY PITTIDAE

Pittas; 23 species

These plump birds have slightly down-curved bills, big heads, short tails and long legs. They are found in tropical forest undergrowth in the Old World. Example:

Gurney's pitta *Pitta gurneyi*: lives in lowland jungles in India. It eats snakes

FAMILY ACANTHISITTIDAE

New Zealand wrens; 3 species

This is a family of small, brown birds which rarely fly higher than about 100 ft; they often scurry along the ground with their tails erect. Example:

New Zealand bush wren *Xenicus longipes*: forages on tree trunks and on the forest floor

FAMILY PHILEPITTIDAE

Asitys; 4 species

These plump, tree-living birds are found only on Madagascar. Mainly fruit-eaters, they sometimes eat insects. They make a hanging nest. Example:

Wattled philepitta or **velvet asity** *Philepitta castanea*: found in humid forests on the eastern slopes of Madagascar up to 5000 ft

FAMILY MENURIDAE

Lyrebirds; 2 species

Brown above and ashen below, these solitary birds have pointed bills and they seldom fly. The male has a long tail with two feathers—up to 24 in. long—forming the frame of the lyre, six pairs of central plumes forming the 'strings' and a web-less central pair of feathers. The male has one of the most elaborate displays of any bird. Example:

Superb lyrebird *Menura superba*: lives in eastern Australia

FAMILY ATRICHORNITHIDAE

Scrub-birds; 2 species

Scrub-birds, which look like wrens with long tails, are related to lyrebirds. They are good mimics and are found only in Australia. The noisy scrub-bird *Atrichornis clamosus*, long feared extinct, was recently rediscovered. Example:

Rufous scrub-bird *Atrichornis rufescens*: lives in eastern Australia

FAMILY ALAUDIDAE

Larks; 70 species

These widely distributed birds have long, pointed wings, rounded, scaly ankles and long, straight hind claws. They always live in open country and nest on the ground. Example:

Skylark *Alauda arvensis*: common in open country in Eurasia and North Africa

FAMILY HIRUNDINIDAE

Swallows and martins; 74 species

This is a family of cosmopolitan birds which resemble swifts but fly more erratically. They have long, pointed wings, weak legs and relatively large mouths with a wide gape; several species have forked tails. They are not good perchers and spend most of their time on the wing. Example:

Barn swallow *Hirundo rustica*: found in North America, Europe, Asia and North Africa. It migrates over enormous distances

FAMILY CAMPEPHAGIDAE

Cuckoo-shrikes; 70 species

These are insect-eating birds from Africa, southern Asia and Australia. They have stout beaks, notched at the tip. Some are as big as pigeons, others as small as sparrows. Example:

Red-shouldered cuckoo-shrike *Campephaga phoenicea*: found in bushy savanna and forest in Africa

Birds

PHYLUM CHORDATA	Animals with notochords
SUB-PHYLUM VERTEBRATA	Animals with backbones
CLASS AVES	Birds
ORDER PASSERIFORMES	Passerines

FAMILY DICRURIDAE
Drongos; 20 species
Drongos are aggressive, insect-eating birds with stout, arched beaks and strong feet; they are found in the tropical forests of the Old World. Example:
African drongo *Dicrurus adsimilis*: found in woodland and savanna

FAMILY ORIOLIDAE
Orioles; 28 species
These birds are found in the forests of Europe and western Asia; they winter in Africa, southern Asia and Australia. The true orioles—different from the American orioles—are generally yellow and black, the males being brighter than the females. They have an undulating flight. Example:
Golden oriole *Oriolus oriolus*: found in woodlands of Eurasia, North Africa and India

FAMILY CORVIDAE
Crows, magpies and jays; 102 species
These aggressive, noisy and usually omnivorous birds are widely distributed. Their ankles are scaled in front and smooth at the back. Examples:
Nutcracker *Nucifraga caryocatactes* ($12\frac{1}{2}$ in.): found in coniferous forests of northern Europe and Asia. It is brown with white specks and feeds on pine seeds
Raven *Corvus corax*: lives in tundra, deciduous forests and sandy deserts in the Northern Hemisphere

FAMILY CALLAEIDAE
Wattlebirds; 3 species
These are New Zealand forest birds with large wattles at the corners of their jaws. They have weak wings. Example:
Kokako or wattled crow *Callaeus cinerea*: leaps from branch to branch in the forest trees

FAMILY GRALLINIDAE
Mudnest-builders; 4 species
The black-and-white Australian birds of this group build deep, open nests of mud on branches. Example:
Magpie-lark *Grallina cyanoleuca*: found near streams and waterways. It feeds on insects and small snails

FAMILY CRACTICIDAE
Song-shrikes; 10 species
Noisy and gregarious, the Australian song-shrikes are strong flyers which impale their prey—insects, lizards and small birds—on thorns to store them. Example:
Black-headed butcher-bird *Cracticus cassicus*: found in open forest and bushy grassland in New Guinea

FAMILY PTILONORHYNCHIDAE
Bowerbirds and catbirds; 18 species
The Australian bowerbirds build huge, often hut-shaped bowers or stages to attract females; they adorn the bowers with bright objects. Example:
Regent bowerbird *Sericulus chrysocephalus*: found in eastern Australian forests; it mixes saliva with plant juices or charcoal to make a 'paint' with which to decorate its bower

FAMILY PARADISAEIDAE
Birds of paradise; 42 species
Relatives of the bowerbirds and crows, these birds live in the northern Australian and New Guinea tropical forests. Most males are ornate and colourful and generally have long tail feathers and crests or ruffs. The females are usually plain. Example:
Lawes' six-wired bird of paradise *Parotia lawesi*: lives in eastern New Guinea high up in forest areas. The male performs his courting display on an area of cleared ground

FAMILY PARIDAE
Tits and chickadees; 59 species
The adaptable and intelligent tits are very small (3–8 in.), with soft, thick plumage which may be grey or black, with blue on the back and yellow on the breast. They have stout, pointed beaks, strong feet and rounded wings. They feed mostly on insects and are found throughout the world except in South America, Australia and Madagascar. Example:
Great tit *Parus major*: found in open woodland throughout Asia and Europe and in the north-west tip of Africa

FAMILY CERTHIIDAE
Tree creepers; 5 species
These slender, brown birds (streaked and spotted above, paler below) have thin, down-curved probing bills and long, stiff tails. They creep up and around the trunks of trees, foraging for the insects on which they feed. Example:
Brown treecreeper *Certhia familiaris*: common in coniferous woodland in North America, Europe and Asia

FAMILY CLIMACTERIDAE
Australian treecreepers; 6 species
The tail feathers of these birds, which live in wooded country in Australia and New Guinea, are not adapted for climbing trees. Some species feed on the ground. Example:
Red-browed treecreeper *Climacteris erythrops*: found in eastern Australia

FAMILY SITTIDAE
Nuthatches; 30 species
These birds are stocky and small, and have thin straight bills, long toes and sharp claws. They are found throughout the world, except in South America and New Zealand. They hunt face downwards on tree trunks for insects and spiders. Northern species also eat seeds, including nuts, in winter. Example:
European nuthatch *Sitta europaea*: common in woodland throughout most of Eurasia

PHYLUM CHORDATA	Animals with notochords
SUB-PHYLUM VERTEBRATA	Animals with backbones
CLASS AVES	Birds
ORDER PASSERIFORMES	Passerines

FAMILY PYCNONOTIDAE
Bulbuls; 120 species
Bulbuls are noisy, drab birds from Africa and southern Asia; they have slender beaks and hair-like feathers on the backs of their necks. Example:
Red-whiskered bulbul *Pycnonotus jocosus*: common in gardens, cities and in wooded countryside in India

FAMILY IRENIDAE
Leafbirds; 14 species
These forest-living, fruit-eating birds from south-east Asia are similar to bulbuls. Example:
Blue-backed fairy bluebird *Irena puella*: found in the upper layers of evergreen forests

FAMILY CINCLIDAE
Dippers; 4 species
Found in cool mountain streams in Eurasia and the Americas, these birds run in and out of the water, capturing small water invertebrates. Example:
Eurasian or **white-breasted dipper** *Cinclus cinclus*: found on mountains in Eurasia

FAMILY TROGLODYTIDAE
Wrens; 60 species
These small ($3\frac{3}{4}$–9 in.), brown birds, most numerous in South America, have slender, sharp beaks, upright tails and a quick strong flight. Example:
Wren *Troglodytes troglodytes*: insect-eating bird of Europe, northern Asia and North America

FAMILY MIMIDAE
Mockingbirds; 34 species
Found living near the ground from Canada to Chile, mockingbirds are good singers and mimics. They build open, cup-shaped nests 2–6 ft above the ground. Both sexes incubate the eggs. Example:
Common mockingbird *Mimus polyglottos*: found in the southern U.S.A. and Central America

FAMILY MUSCICAPIDAE
Flycatchers, babblers, thrushes and warblers; about 1200 species
Most members of this huge family are Old World, insect-eating birds characterised by ten primary wing feathers. Examples:
Nightingale *Luscinia megarhynchos* ($6\frac{1}{2}$ in.): found in woodland undergrowth in southern Europe, western Asia and north-west Africa
Blackcap *Sylvia atricapilla* ($5\frac{1}{2}$ in.): found in woodlands in western Asia, north-west Africa and Atlantic islands
Spotted flycatcher *Muscicapa striata*: lives in forests and wooded grasslands in western Eurasia and north-west Africa. It hunts flying insects from a perch
Grey-sided laughing thrush *Garrula caerulatus* (12 in.): lives in forests, ranging from the Himalayan area to Taiwan

FAMILY PRUNELLIDAE
Accentors; 12 species
Stout, drab birds with thin beaks and rounded wings, the accentors are found only in Eurasia and are typical of Arctic regions. Example:
Hedge sparrow *Prunella modularis*: widespread in Europe and western Asia

FAMILY MOTACILLIDAE
Wagtails and pipits; 48 species
These slender birds with thin, pointed beaks, walk along the ground and are found throughout the world. Example:
Grey wagtail *Motacilla cinerea*: found near streams in Eurasia and the north-west corner of Africa

FAMILY BOMBYCILLIDAE
Waxwings and palmchats; 9 species
This is a family of fruit-eating birds of the Northern Hemisphere; they have broad beaks and silky plumage. Example:
Bohemian waxwing *Bombycilla garrulus*: lives in coniferous forests in Europe, Asia and North America

FAMILY ARTAMIDAE
Wood-swallows; 10 species
These small birds of south-east Asia and Australia have long, pointed wings; they catch insects in flight. Example:
White-browed wood-swallow *Artamus superciliosus*: nests in rock crevices or hollow trees in Australia

FAMILY VANGIDAE
Vanga-shrikes; 12 species
A Madagascar family of blue-and-white or black-and-white birds with rounded wings and short tails. The species vary in size from 5 to 12 in. Their beaks also vary considerably, though all are strongly made and hooked. Example:
Hook-billed vanga-shrike *Vanga curvirostris*: lives in forests and grasslands. It is an insect-eater which also takes small frogs and lizards

FAMILY LANIIDAE
Shrikes; 74 species
These miniature birds of prey, found in Europe, Asia, Africa and North America, kill insects and small vertebrates with their sharp, hooked beaks and often impale their prey on thorns. Example:
Great grey or **northern shrike** *Lanius excubitor*: breeds in Canada; winters in the United States

FAMILY STURNIDAE
Starlings; 110 species
This is an Old World, largely tropical family of active and highly gregarious birds with straight or slightly down-curved beaks. Their flight is strong and direct. Example:
Hill mynah *Gracula religiosa*: a fruit-eating bird from the forests of southern Asia. It is a close relative of the common starling

CLASSIFICATION

Birds

PHYLUM CHORDATA	Animals with notochords
SUB-PHYLUM VERTEBRATA	Animals with backbones
CLASS AVES	Birds
ORDER PASSERIFORMES	Passerines

FAMILY MELIPHAGIDAE

Honey-eaters; 167 species

Honey-eaters are small, often patterned, birds from Australia, the Pacific islands and southern Africa. They have slender, down-curved beaks and tube-like, brush-tipped tongues adapted for feeding on nectar and insects. Example:

White-bearded honey-eater *Meliornis novaehollandiae*: found in scrubland, open forest and sometimes swampy areas, from southern Queensland to Tasmania

FAMILY NECTARINIIDAE

Sunbirds; 106 species

Sunbirds are the gaudy, Old World counterparts of the New World hummingbirds, but they usually perch on, rather than hover above, flowers; some are known as spider-hunters. Their nests are always suspended from leaves or branches of trees. Example:

Scarlet-chested sunbird *Chalcomitra senegalensis*: found in the savannas of Africa

FAMILY DICAEIDAE

Flowerpeckers; 55 species

These are plump, active birds from south-east Asia and Australia; they have tubular tongues and shorter beaks than the sunbirds. Example:

Yellow-tailed diamond bird *Pardalotus punctatus*: found only in the forests of south-eastern Australia

FAMILY ZOSTEROPIDAE

White-eyes; 85 species

These nectar-eaters, with brush-tipped tongues, narrow white rings round the eyes, and nine primary wing feathers, are found throughout the Old World tropics. Gregarious birds, they often travel in large flocks. Example:

Oriental white-eye *Zosterops palpebrosa*: found in woody country and ever-green forests up to 8000 ft from India to the Philippines

FAMILY VIREONIDAE

Vireos; 45 species

This family of small green birds, 4–6 in. long, live among trees in the New World. The North American species usually migrate to the tropics in winter. Example:

Yellow-throated vireo *Vireo flavifrons*: found in the deciduous forests of eastern North America

FAMILY DREPANIDIDAE

Hawaiian honeycreepers; 22 species

This recently evolved group has radiated from a single colonist species. The males are brightly coloured in green, red, yellow, grey or black; the females are duller and grey-green. Honeycreepers have beaks and tongues of various shapes. Example:

Hawaiian honeycreeper or **iiwi** *Vestiaria coccinea*: found in flowering trees, where it feeds on nectar and insects for food

FAMILY PARULIDAE

Wood-warblers; 113 species

This group exhibits a wide range of social, feeding and breeding behaviour. They also vary greatly in size—from 4 to 21 in.—but all have conical beaks. They are found throughout the New World. Example:

Magnolia warbler *Dendroica magnolia*: breeds in Canadian coniferous forests

FAMILY ICTERIDAE

American orioles; 87 species

New World birds found from Alaska to Argentina. They are small, with slender, pointed beaks. The North American species are migratory, often travelling in huge, mixed flocks. The tropical species do not migrate. A number of species regularly interbreed in the wild. Example:

Troupial *Icterus icterus*: an outstanding songster found in northern South America

FAMILY EMBERIZIDAE

Tanagers, cardinals, sugarbirds and buntings; 525 species

This is a diverse group of birds found in Europe, Asia and America; it includes many brightly coloured species. Examples:

Paradise tanager *Tangara chilensis* (5½ in.): found in tropical South America east of the Andes

Cardinal *Richmondena cardinalis*: found in North America

FAMILY FRINGILLIDAE

Finches; 138 species

These tree-loving seed-eaters make open cup nests. They are found throughout the world, except in Australia; many are migratory. Examples:

Chaffinch *Fringilla coelebs*: found in forests and cultivated areas in Europe, North Africa and western Asia

Cactus ground finch *Geospiza scandens* (5 in.): one of Darwin's finches from the Galapagos Islands, where it feeds on cactus

FAMILY ESTRILDIDAE

Weaver-finches; 108 species

These small seed-eaters of the Old World tropics make solitary, untidy nests. Example:

Gouldian finch *Poephila gouldiae*: found in Australia

FAMILY PLOCEIDAE

Weavers and sparrows; 132 species

Members of this family, found in Europe, Asia and Africa, often in large colonies. Examples:

House sparrow *Passer domesticus* (6 in.): found originally in Europe, Asia and Africa; has been introduced into Australia and North America, where it is now a pest. It eats seeds and insects

Red bishop *Euplectes orix*: found in southern and eastern Africa. The male has brilliant orange-red colouring

CLASSIFICATION

Mammals

PHYLUM CHORDATA	Animals with notochords	ORDER MONOTREMATA	Egg-laying mammals
SUB-PHYLUM VERTEBRATA	Animals with backbones	SUB-CLASS THERIA	Mammals that do not lay eggs
CLASS MAMMALIA	Mammals	INFRA-CLASS METATHERIA	Marsupials
SUB-CLASS PROTOTHERIA	Monotremes	ORDER MARSUPIALIA	Pouched mammals

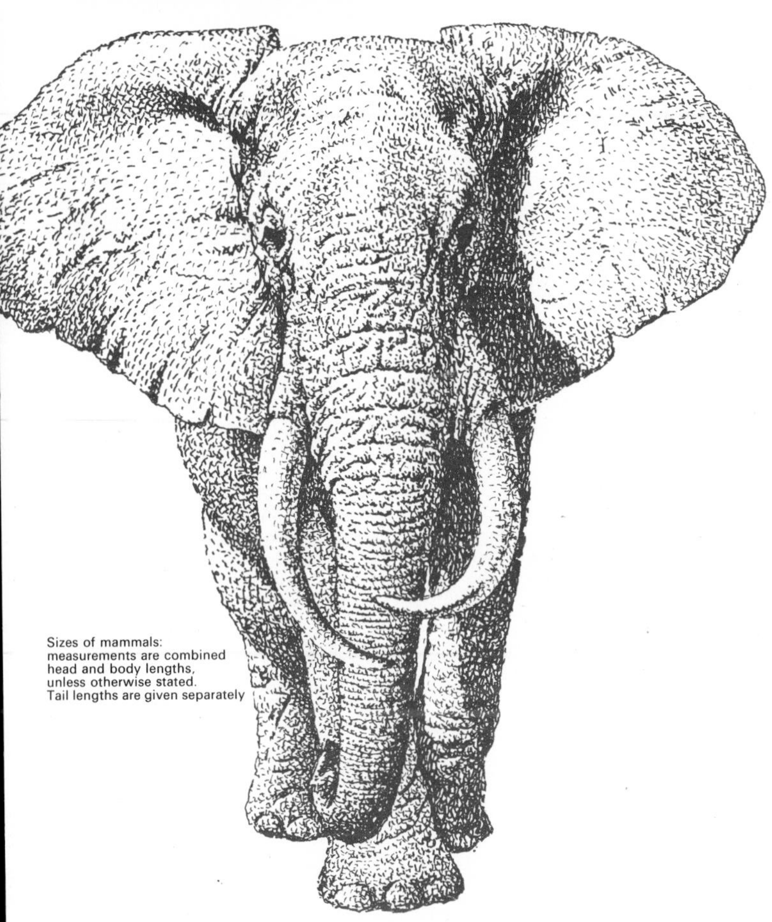

Sizes of mammals: measurements are combined head and body lengths, unless otherwise stated. Tail lengths are given separately

A typical mammal is a warm-blooded, air breathing vertebrate. The heart is divided into four chambers. The body temperature is regulated by a mechanism in the brain, and maintained by the body hair. Young mammals are suckled on milk from the mother's mammary glands. The basic anatomical distinction between mammals and reptiles is the presence of only one bone in the lower jaw—reptiles have more than one. Bones inside the ears of mammals have evolved from the additional jaw bones of reptiles.

Living mammals are classified as monotremes, or egg-laying mammals; marsupials, whose offspring are born at an early stage of development and complete their development attached to a nipple, generally in the mother's pouch; and placentals, whose offspring are nourished throughout their embryonic stage by means of a placenta and are born at an advanced stage of development.

Nearly half the living species of mammals are rodents, and about another quarter are bats.

SUB-CLASS PROTOTHERIA

This group of primitive mammals has only one order:

ORDER MONOTREMATA

Egg-laying mammals

Monotremes, the most primitive living mammals, are the only ones that lay eggs. They do not have the bridge of nerve tissue that connects the hemispheres of the brain in more advanced mammals. Like reptiles, they have only one posterior opening to the body—the anal and urinogenital apertures open into a common chamber at the end of the gut. But the way in which they regulate their body temperatures is more like that of mammals than of reptiles. The control is fairly constant when the external temperature is between about 28 and 32°C (82 and 90°F), but outside these limits it tends to vary. They possess rudimentary bones typical of marsupials, such as those that support the pouch in kangaroos. After hatching, the young are nourished on milk from teatless mammary glands. In living forms there are no functional teeth in the adult, and the male has a horny spur on each ankle, which in the platypus is grooved underneath and connects with a poison gland. There are two families:

FAMILY TACHYGLOSSIDAE

Spiny anteaters or echidnas; 5 species

Echidnas are burrowers with broad feet and small eyes. They are covered with short, barbless spines, except on the belly. The snout is long and tubular, and the long, sticky tongue, used to sweep up ants, has horny serrations which grind against ridges on the palate; there are no teeth. In the breeding season, the female develops a pouch into which she puts her egg (generally only one but sometimes two or three). Echidnas occur in New Guinea, Australia and Tasmania. Example:
Australian spiny anteater *Tachyglossus aculeatus*: an echidna found throughout Australia

FAMILY ORNITHORHYNCHIDAE

There is one species:
Platypus *Ornithorhynchus anatinus*: found in rivers in eastern Australia and Tasmania. It is well adapted to life in water, with dense underfur, a flattened tail, webbed feet, no external ears and a sensitive bill covered with soft, rubbery skin

ORDER MONOTREMATA
Egg-laying mammals

Australian spiny anteater
Tachyglossus aculeatus
18 in.

Platypus
Ornithorhynchus anatinus
18 in., tail 6 in.

SUB-CLASS THERIA

This group contains the majority of living mammals, which do not lay eggs. There are two infra-classes:

INFRA-CLASS METATHERIA

There is one order:

ORDER MARSUPIALIA

Pouched mammals

These animals have bones to support a pouch, but not all have external pouches. The young are born at such an early stage of development that the short period of gestation in the womb is followed by a further development period. The mother licks a path in her fur from the base of the tail to the teats, which are in the pouch when there is one, and the offspring crawls along and attaches itself to a teat. Like monotremes, marsupials have no nerve tissue connecting the hemispheres of the brain. There are nine families:

FAMILY DIDELPHIDAE

Opossums; 65 species

These largely tree-dwelling animals, ranging from south-eastern Canada to Argentina, have a large, clawless great toe, set like a thumb in opposition to the other four digits. Most species have no pouch, and their gestation period is the shortest of any mammal—only 12–13 days. Opossums have 50 teeth. Examples:
Water opossum or **yapok** *Chironectes minimus*: found in South American streams and lakes
Virginian or **common opossum** *Didelphis marsupialis* (20 in., tail 9–20 in.): lives near lakes, streams and swamps from eastern U.S.A. to South America

FAMILY DASYURIDAE

Australian native cats and marsupial mice; 45 species

A family of mammals whose pouch, if there is one, is poorly developed or conspicuous only in the breeding season. Examples:
Fat-tailed marsupial mouse *Sminthopsis crassicaudata*: found in south-western and south-eastern Australia. It is mainly insect-eating
Eastern native cat *Dasyurus viverrinus* (17 in., tail 11 in.): common in forests and grasslands in Tasmania; also found in southern Australia. It is a grey-brown nocturnal animal with light spots

FAMILY MYRMECOBIIDAE

There is one species:
Numbat or **banded anteater** *Myrmecobius fasciatus*: found in western and southern Australia in open forest and scrub. A red-brown animal with six or seven white bands, a long tail and no pouch, it feeds on ants and termites

FAMILY NOTORYCTIDAE

Marsupial moles; 2 species

Australian burrowing mammals. Example:
Southern marsupial mole *Notoryctes typhlops*: inhabits deserts in South Australia. This mole-like animal has a horny knob on its short tail, and a horny shield on its nose which protects it when it digs its shallow burrows

FAMILY PERAMELIDAE

Bandicoots; 19 species

Bandicoots, found in Ceram, New Guinea, Australia and Tasmania, have long, pointed flexible muzzles with which they root in the soil. Their ears are often large and their hind limbs are long. Example:
Long-nosed bandicoot *Perameles nasuta*: found in eastern Australia

ORDER MARSUPIALIA
Pouched mammals

Water opossum or **yapok**
Chironectes minimus
13 in., tail 16 in.

Numbat or **banded anteater**
Myrmecobius fasciatus
10 in., tail 7 in.

Fat-tailed marsupial mouse
Sminthopsis crassicaudata
3½ in., tail 4 in.

Long-nosed bandicoot
Perameles nasuta
16 in., tail 5 in.

Southern marsupial mole
Notoryctes typhlops
5½ in., tail 1 in.

CLASSIFICATION

Mammals

PHYLUM CHORDATA	Animals with notochords
SUB-PHYLUM VERTEBRATA	Animals with backbones
CLASS MAMMALIA	Mammals
SUB-CLASS THERIA	Mammals that do not lay eggs
INFRA-CLASS METATHERIA	Marsupials

ORDER MARSUPIALIA	Pouched mammals
INFRA-CLASS EUTHERIA	Placental mammals
ORDER INSECTIVORA	Insect-eating mammals
ORDER DERMOPTERA	Colugos

FAMILY CAENOLESTIDAE
Rat opossums; 7 species
These shrew-like marsupials from the forests of South America are the only marsupials apart from the opossums outside Australasia. They have long heads and long sensory whiskers. Example:
Chilean rat opossum *Rhyncholestes raphanurus*: a rare species, found only in the dense forests in the province of Llanquihue and on Chiloe Island, Chile

FAMILY PHALANGERIDAE
Phalangers or possums; 45 species
These tree-dwelling, plant-eating mammals are found from Timor and Celebes to Tasmania. Examples:
Koala *Phascolarctos cinereus* (2 ft 8 in., rudimentary tail): confined to the eucalyptus forests of eastern Australia. It has woolly fur, large ears, a soft pad on the nose and the female has a rearward-opening pouch
Brush-tailed possum *Trichosurus vulpecula*: occurs widely in Australia, usually in forests, open woodland or trees growing in grassland

FAMILY VOMBATIDAE
Wombats; 2 species
Wombats are large, burrowing, tail-less mammals with rodent-like grinding teeth. Some of their burrows extend for as much as 100 ft. Example:
Hairy-nosed wombat *Lasiorhinus latifrons*: found in hilly regions of south-eastern Queensland and in southern parts of South Australia. It sleeps during the day in long burrows

FAMILY MACROPODIDAE
Kangaroos; 52 species
Kangaroos, found in Australia, Tasmania and New Guinea, have small heads, large ears and long hind limbs and feet (the family name means 'large-footed' animals). The tail, usually thick at the base, is used as a prop or additional leg, and to balance the kangaroo when it leaps. Examples:
Brush-tailed rock wallaby *Petrogale penicillata* (2 ft 5 in., tail 23 in.): lives on boulder-strewn outcrops in dry forests of eastern Australia. It is a nocturnal animal with a long, slender tail, not thickened at the base
Red kangaroo *Megaleia rufa*: occurs in open grasslands throughout most of Australia. The males have red fur, whereas the females are blue-grey

INFRA-CLASS EUTHERIA

This group contains the placental mammals, which nourish their growing embryos for a comparatively long period of gestation through a complete placenta (as opposed to the incomplete placenta of marsupials) attached to the wall of the womb. There are 19 orders:

ORDER INSECTIVORA

Insect-eating mammals
Most members of this loosely knit group are small, primitive mammals with a long, sensitive snout, clawed toes, and the cheek teeth have sharp, conical cusps, enabling them to seize and crush insects. Most members of the order have five toes on each foot. There are eight families:

FAMILY SOLENODONTIDAE
Solenodons; 2 species
These are comparatively large, stoutly built nocturnal animals with long, nearly naked tails and very long snouts. Example:
Haitian solenodon *Solenodon paradoxus*: occurs in the forests and bush in Haiti. The other species lives in Cuba

FAMILY TENRECIDAE
Tenrecs; 20 species
Superficially like small solenodons, tenrecs have long, pointed snouts and live on Madagascar and the nearby Comoro Islands. Some species are spiny and some are burrowing. Example:
Long-tailed tenrec *Microgale longicaudata*: inhabits forests on Madagascar

FAMILY POTAMOGALIDAE
Otter shrews; 3 species
Externally resembling small otters, these mammals, found only in tropical Africa, have soft fur with a protective coat of coarse guard hairs. They eat small fish and crustaceans. Example:
Giant otter shrew *Potamogale velox*: found in the African forest rivers

FAMILY CHRYSOCHLORIDAE
Golden moles; 20 species
These mammals are the African equivalent of the true moles. They have thick fur with a metallic golden to violet lustre, loose skin, a smooth leathery pad on the muzzle, used for burrowing into the soil, eyes covered with hairy skin, and small ears concealed by fur. They feed mainly on worms and insects. Example:
Cape golden mole *Chrysochloris asiatica*: found in southern Africa

FAMILY ERINACEIDAE
Hedgehogs; 15 species
Hedgehogs are covered with short, barbless spines, except on the belly, and when disturbed they can roll into a ball for protection. They range throughout Europe, Africa and Asia. Examples:
Desert hedgehog *Paraechinus aethiopicus*: found in northern Africa and the Middle East in desert areas
Gymnure or **Malayan moon-rat** *Echinosorex gymnurus* (12 in., tail 9 in.): found near streams in forests of south-eastern Asia. It has a naked tail, flattened at the end for swimming, a narrow body, a long nose, and a harsh (not actually prickly) coat

FAMILY SORICIDAE
Shrews; more than 200 species
Shrews are small, short-legged mammals with a long, pointed nose, short dense fur, and small weak eyes. They are found throughout the world except in Australia and polar regions. Examples:
Lesser white-toothed shrew *Crocidura suaveolens* (3 in., tail 1 in.): ranges from Europe to eastern Asia. The tips of its teeth are white
Common shrew *Sorex araneus*: ranges through moist areas of Europe and Asia. It has sleek fur, and teeth with brown or purple tips

FAMILY TALPIDAE
Moles; 19 species
The short, thick, cylindrical body, minute eyes and ears, short neck and short, stout limbs of moles help make them highly efficient burrowers. The front feet, turned permanently outwards, move the earth aside with a breast-stroke action. The velvety fur will lie in any direction, and moles can move backwards as well as forwards in their tunnels. Example:
Common Eurasian mole *Talpa europaea*: found in Europe and Asia

FAMILY MACROSCELIDIDAE
Elephant shrews; 14 species
Elephant shrews, found only in Africa, are rat-sized animals with a long, scaly tail, a long, sensitive snout, and large eyes. Most are active during the day, taking refuge at night in burrows of other animals or in holes in the ground. The young are well developed at birth and can walk almost immediately. Elephant-shrews eat insects, eggs and small mammals. Example:
Rufous elephant shrew *Elephantulus rufescens*: occurs in grasslands in eastern Africa. It runs along the ground, using its powerful, long hind limbs

ORDER DERMOPTERA

This order contains a single family, consisting of two species of colugos; both of them are found in the tropical forest of eastern Asia

FAMILY CYNOCEPHALIDAE
Colugos; 2 species
These slender-limbed mammals have a large, gliding membrane attached to the neck and sides of the body and extending to the tips of the fingers, the sharp-clawed toes, and the tail. Some of their lower teeth slope outwards and are comb-like in form; they are used for grooming and for straining food. Colugos spend the day hanging head-upwards from branches, and become active at night, when they feed on fruit, buds and leaves, often gliding as far as 70 yds from tree to tree. Example:
Philippines colugo or **flying lemur** *Cynocephalus volans*: confined to forests in the Philippines. The other species lives in parts of Indo-China, Indonesia and Malaysia

Philippines colugo
Cynocephalus volans
17 in., tail 11 in.

ORDER MARSUPIALIA
Pouched mammals

Chilean rat opossum *Rhyncholestes raphanurus* 5 in., tail 3½ in.
Brush-tailed possum *Trichosurus vulpecula* 18 in., tail 11 in.
Hairy-nosed wombat *Lasiorhinus latifrons* 3 ft 6 in.
Red kangaroo *Megaleia rufa* 5 ft, tail 3 ft 6 in.

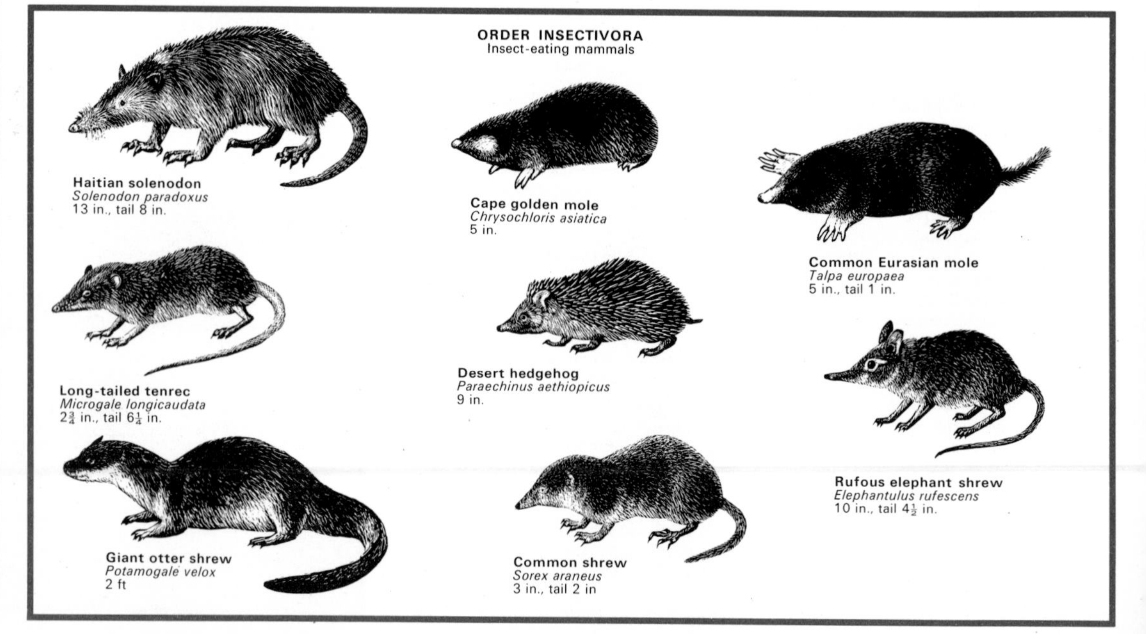

ORDER INSECTIVORA
Insect-eating mammals

Haitian solenodon *Solenodon paradoxus* 13 in., tail 8 in.
Long-tailed tenrec *Microgale longicaudata* 2¾ in., tail 6¼ in.
Giant otter shrew *Potamogale velox* 2 ft
Cape golden mole *Chrysochloris asiatica* 5 in.
Desert hedgehog *Paraechinus aethiopicus* 9 in.
Common shrew *Sorex araneus* 3 in., tail 2 in
Common Eurasian mole *Talpa europaea* 5 in., tail 1 in.
Rufous elephant shrew *Elephantulus rufescens* 10 in., tail 4½ in.

PHYLUM CHORDATA	Animals with notochords
SUB-PHYLUM VERTEBRATA	Animals with backbones
CLASS MAMMALIA	Mammals
SUB-CLASS THERIA	Mammals that do not lay eggs
INFRA-CLASS EUTHERIA	Placental mammals
ORDER CHIROPTERA	Bats

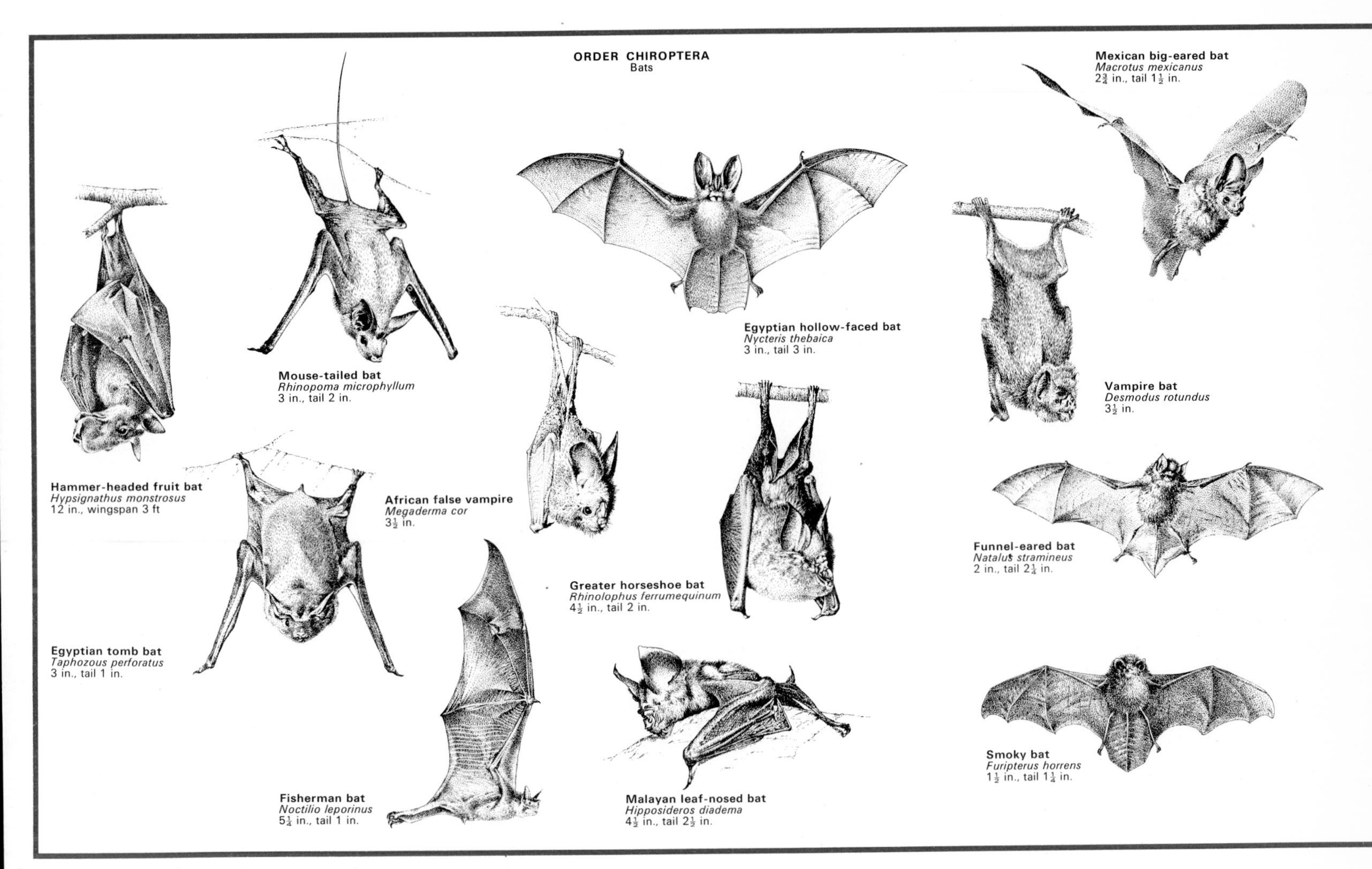

ORDER CHIROPTERA

Bats

Bats are the only flying mammals. The paper-thin, elastic membranes extending from the sides of the body, legs and tail are extensions of the skin on the belly and back; sometimes the tail is very loosely connected with the membrane which stretches from heel to heel. There are two sub-orders:

SUB-ORDER MEGACHIROPTERA

Fruit-eating bats

This sub-order contains a single family of bats that feed mainly on fruit and nectar

FAMILY PTEROPODIDAE

Old World fruit bats and flying foxes; 130 species

Members of this family, found in the tropics and sub-tropics, have short, rudimentary tails and generally a claw on the second as well as the first finger. By day they hang in trees, emerging at night to forage for food. Example:

Hammer-headed fruit bat *Hypsignathus monstrosus*: found in forests from Uganda to West Africa. The adult male has a large, square head, a thick muzzle, huge pendulous lips, ruffles round the nose, a warty snout, a hairless split chin and highly developed voice organs which produce a continual croaking and quacking, probably to attract the female

SUB-ORDER MICROCHIROPTERA

Members of this sub-order are small or medium-sized bats with small eyes, comparatively short snouts and no claw on the second finger. Most have flaps in front of their large ears, which are used for navigation and detecting flying prey by echo-location. There are 16 families:

FAMILY RHINOPOMATIDAE

Mouse-tailed bats; 4 species

The bats of the single genus in this family have a tail nearly as long as the head and body together. Example:

Rhinopoma microphyllum: found in the Old World tropics

FAMILY EMBALLONURIDAE

Sheath-tailed bats; 50 species

Many of these rather small tropical bats have glandular wing-sacs secreting a strong-smelling red substance; these are more developed in the male and may serve to attract the female. The tip of the tail is free of skin, so that in flight the tail membrane can be lengthened by stretching out the hind legs. Example:

Egyptian tomb bat *Taphozous perforatus*: found in north-east Africa and India, they begin feeding at dusk

FAMILY NOCTILIONIDAE

Bulldog bats; 2 species

Bats of this family have full, swollen-looking lips, the upper lip being divided by a fold of skin. They have long, narrow wings. Example:

Fisherman bat *Noctilio leporinus*: ranges from Mexico southwards to Brazil, patrolling the sea and fresh waters and catching fish in its claws

FAMILY NYCTERIDAE

Slit-faced bats; 10 species

These bats have long, loose fur, large ears and a furrow extending from the nostrils to between the eyes, ending in a deep pit in the forehead. The tail has a T-shaped tip, a unique feature among mammals. Example:

Egyptian hollow-faced bat *Nycteris thebaica*: found in Corfu, Africa and south-west Asia

FAMILY MEGADERMATIDAE

False vampires; 5 species

Once thought to be blood-suckers, these bats eat insects and small vertebrates. They have a divided lobe in front of the ear and the leaf-like appendage known as a nose-leaf, which the bats use in echo-location, is long and erect in this family. Example:

African false vampire *Megaderma cor*: roosts in large numbers in caves and trees from Ethiopia to Tanzania

FAMILY RHINOLOPHIDAE

Horseshoe bats; 50 species

These bats, found in the Old World as far eastwards as Australia, have a very complex nose-leaf extending over the upper lip, round the nostrils, and coming to a point above them. Example:

Greater horseshoe bat *Rhinolophus ferrumequinum*: occurs in the Mediterranean region and western Europe, including southern England

FAMILY HIPPOSIDERIDAE

Leaf-nosed bats; 100 species

This family is closely related to the horseshoe bats. Its members are found in Africa and southern Asia. Some species hibernate. Example:

Malayan leaf-nosed bat *Hipposideros diadema*: roosts in hollow trees, caves and buildings

FAMILY PHYLLOSTOMATIDAE

American leaf-nosed bats; about 100 species

The nose-leaf of these bats, which feed on insects, fruit and nectar, is sometimes absent. Some have a long nose and tongue with which they extract nectar from flowers. Example:

Mexican big-eared bat *Macrotus mexicanus*: ranges through western and southern Mexico to Guatemala

FAMILY DESMODONTIDAE

Vampires; 3 species

Members of this family have no nose-leaf but have instead a naked pad with U-shaped grooves at the tip. The teeth are specialised for cutting, and these are the true vampires which feed on fresh blood. They bite their prey where hair or feathers are scanty, usually without disturbing the sleeping victim. Example:

Vampire bat *Desmodus rotundus*: found from northern Mexico to Chile, central Argentina and Uruguay

FAMILY NATALIDAE

Funnel-eared bats; about 15 species

These slim bats have large, funnel-shaped ears. Example:

Natalus stramineus: a funnel-eared bat found from northern Mexico to Panama; also in Brazil, the Guianas and the Lesser Antilles

FAMILY FURIPTERIDAE

Smoky bats; 2 species

A tropical South American family of small funnel-eared bats with truncated snouts ending in a disc or pad. Example:

Smoky bat *Furipterus horrens*: occurs from Panama southwards to Brazil

CLASSIFICATION

Mammals

PHYLUM CHORDATA	Animals with notochords
SUB-PHYLUM VERTEBRATA	Animals with backbones
CLASS MAMMALIA	Mammals
INFRA-CLASS EUTHERIA	Placental mammals
ORDER CHIROPTERA	Bats
ORDER PRIMATES	Primates

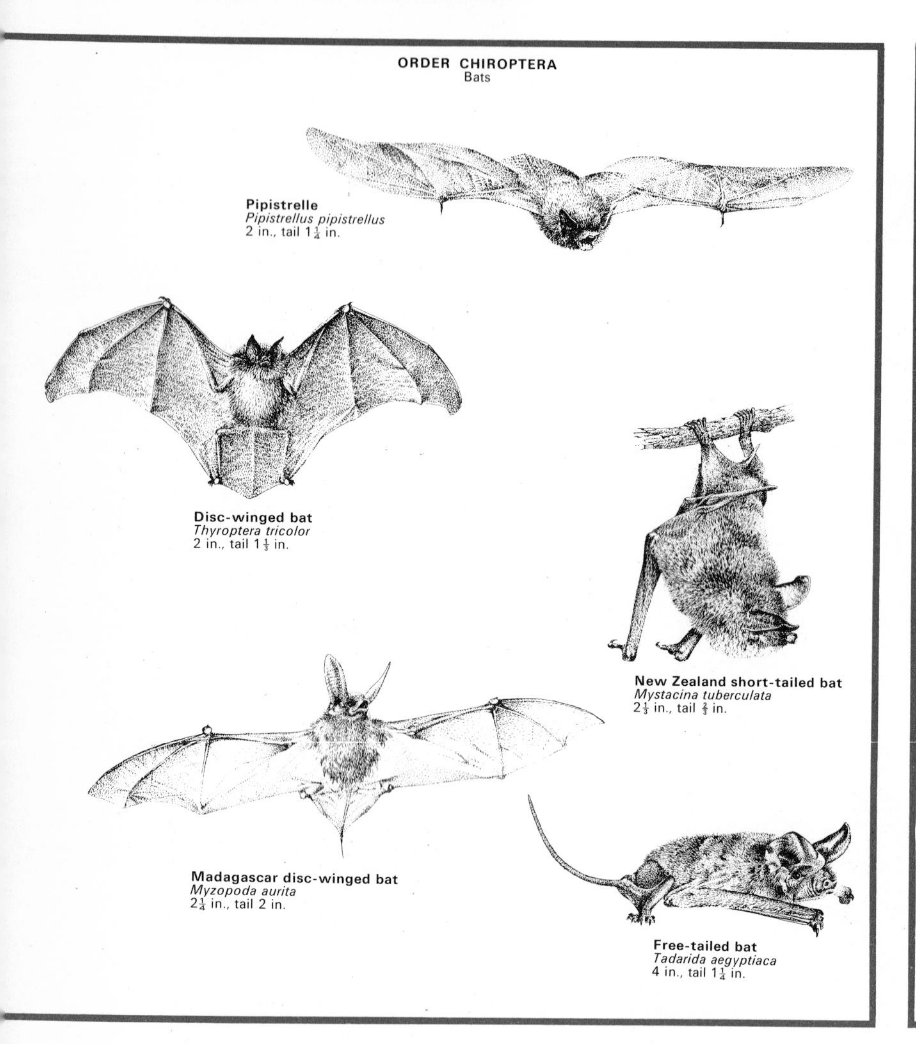

ORDER CHIROPTERA
Bats

Pipistrelle
Pipistrellus pipistrellus
2 in., tail $1\frac{1}{4}$ in.

Disc-winged bat
Thyroptera tricolor
2 in., tail $1\frac{1}{3}$ in.

New Zealand short-tailed bat
Mystacina tuberculata
$2\frac{1}{3}$ in., tail $\frac{2}{3}$ in.

Madagascar disc-winged bat
Myzopoda aurita
$2\frac{1}{4}$ in., tail 2 in.

Free-tailed bat
Tadarida aegyptiaca
4 in., tail $1\frac{1}{4}$ in.

Philippine tree-shrew
Urogale everetti
8 in., tail 6 in.

Indri
Indri indri
2 ft 6 in., tail $2\frac{1}{2}$ in.

Ruffed lemur
Varecia variegata
24 in., tail 24 in.

Aye-aye
Daubentonia madagascariensis
16 in., tail 24 in.

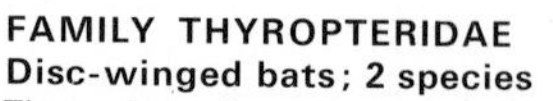

FAMILY THYROPTERIDAE

Disc-winged bats; 2 species

These bats from central and northern South America have circular suction discs or cups on the wrists and ankles, and claws on the thumbs. Example:

Thyroptera tricolor: found in tropical forests from British Honduras south-eastwards to Trinidad

FAMILY MYZOPODIDAE

There is one species:

Madagascar disc-winged bat *Myzopoda aurita*: similar to the true disc-winged bats, but with larger ears and the thumb-claw is shorter

FAMILY VESPERTILIONIDAE

Typical insect-eating bats; 275 species

The four previous families are probably specialised off-shoots of the Vespertilionidae, a family of very small bats with tiny eyes, and generally without a nose-leaf. Some have glands in the snout and some have long ears. Examples:

Noctule *Nyctalus noctula* (3 in., tail $2\frac{1}{2}$ in.): found in Europe and Asia. It is red-brown, and it flies with many quick turns, often before sunset. It often roosts in very large colonies

Long-eared bat *Plecotus auritus* (2 in., tail 2 in.): found in Europe and Asia. Except in summer, when females form colonies, it roosts singly. It flies only after dark and can hover

Pipistrelle *Pipistrellus pipistrellus*: occurs in Europe and Asia. Generally dark brown in colour, it usually appears about sunset. Its flight is jerky and erratic, and it roosts in cave entrances, under rocks, in trees and in buildings

FAMILY MYSTACINIDAE

There is one species:

New Zealand short-tailed bat *Mystacina tuberculata*: today found only on Solomon Island, off Stewart Island. It has needle-sharp claws, those of the thumbs and feet bearing small subsidiary talons. The wings are rolled up under a leathery membrane when the bat is not flying; this allows the arms to be used in running

FAMILY MOLOSSIDAE

Mastiff or free-tailed bats; 80 species

Most members of this family, found in most warm parts of the world, have tails which project beyond the edge of the tail membrane, narrow wings, velvety fur and no nose-leaf. Example:

Tadarida aegyptiaca: a free-tailed bat found in Africa and western Asia. It sleeps by day in hollow trees and crevices in caves and rocks

ORDER PRIMATES

Most primates are relatively unspecialised, tree-dwelling mammals, having limbs with five digits but showing a tendency towards the development of grasping hands and feet. They generally have nails instead of claws. The eyes are near the front of the head and set close together so that both look in the same direction—providing stereoscopic vision and judgment of distances—and the sense of smell is less important than the senses of vision, hearing and touch. Apart from man, whose distribution is world-wide, most primates live in tropical and sub-tropical regions. There are two sub-orders:

SUB-ORDER PROSIMII

This sub-order contains the more primitive primates, which have long snouts and eyes which do not face directly forwards. There are six families:

FAMILY TUPAIIDAE

Tree-shrews; 20 species

This ancient family is sometimes included with the insect-eating mammals. Tree-shrews outwardly look like long-nosed squirrels. The scrotum, unlike that of other primates, lies in front of the penis. They have long and supple digits with sharp, moderately curved claws. All live in tropical forests in Asia. Example:

Philippine tree-shrew *Urogale everetti*: found only on Mindanao Island

FAMILY LEMURIDAE

Lemurs; 15 species

They are the most abundant of the primates of Madagascar. Their lower incisor teeth are modified to form a fur-grooming comb, unlike those of the tree-shrews. The fingers and toes bear nails, but there is a long grooming claw on each second toe. The thumb and big toe are opposable to the other digits. Examples:

Ruffed lemur *Varecia variegata*: lives in forests of north-eastern Madagascar. It has a ruff of long hair on its neck and the sides of its head. There are three differently coloured races

Grey mouse lemur *Microcebus murinus* (5 in., tail $6\frac{1}{2}$ in.): occurs in the forests of western Madagascar. Mouse lemurs, the smallest primates, are agile and active at night, preying on insects. It is possible that they are related to the bush-babies of Africa and many aspects of their behaviour are similar

FAMILY INDRIIDAE

Members of this family are similar to lemurs except that they climb with a hand-over-hand movement, cling in an erect position to vertical branches, and move on the ground by hopping because their legs are much longer than their arms. Strictly vegetarian, they feed on leaves and fruit. Example:

Indri and sifakas; 4 species

Indri *Indri indri*: now very rare, it is confined to the forests of eastern Madagascar. Active by day, it has a mournful, wailing territorial call

FAMILY DAUBENTONIIDAE

There is one species:

Aye-aye *Daubentonia madagascariensis*: found in forests of northern Madagascar. The aye-aye has a single rodent-like incisor on each side of each jaw, and gnaws a hole in bark where its sensitive ears have located an insect; it then inserts its wiry middle finger and impales a grub

FAMILY LORISIDAE

Lorises, pottos and bush-babies; 11 species

Lorises and pottos are well adapted for slow movement, so that they can creep up undetected on birds. Their hands and feet are specialised for grasping; the first digit is opposable and very strong. Bush-babies have long tails, large eyes, and large mobile ears which can be folded. They are vertical clingers, and they tend to hop on their hind legs when on the ground. All are nocturnal. Like lemurs they have a tooth comb. Example:

Slender loris *Loris tardigradus*: found in southern India and Ceylon. It is a slender animal and has no tail

PHYLUM CHORDATA	Animals with notochords
SUB-PHYLUM VERTEBRATA	Animals with backbones
CLASS MAMMALIA	Mammals
INFRA-CLASS EUTHERIA	Placental mammals
ORDER PRIMATES	Primates

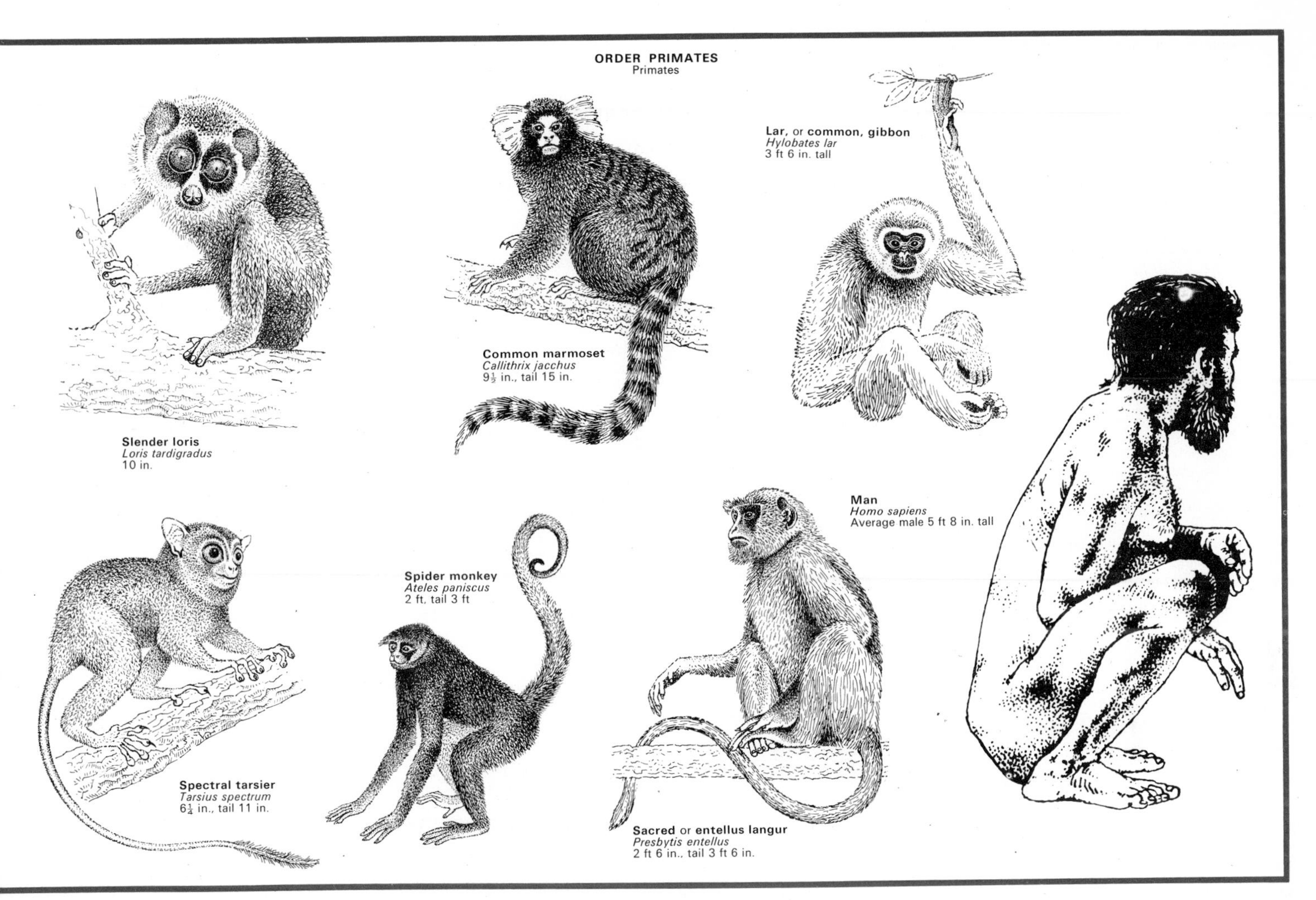

FAMILY TARSIIDAE
Tarsiers; 3 species

Tarsiers have flattened faces, very large eyes, round skulls and no tooth comb. The legs are elongated, especially the tarsus bones, and the scaly, naked underside of the tail is used to provide support. Tarsiers are active only at night, when they leap through the trees from trunk to trunk. All live in south-east Asia. Example:

Spectral tarsier *Tarsius spectrum*: found in scrub jungle in Celebes and neighbouring islands

SUB-ORDER ANTHROPOIDEA

This sub-order includes the higher primates, which possess a short snout and full stereoscopic vision. It is divided into two infra-orders: the Platyrrhini (the first two families) and the Catarrhini (the three other families), which may have evolved independently from prosimians. The platyrrhines, with wide-apart, sideways-facing nostrils, are entirely South American, whereas the catarrhines, with close-together, downward-facing nostrils, are found in Africa and Asia

FAMILY CALLITRICHIDAE
Marmosets and tamarins; 21 species

These small monkeys have claws on all digits except the great toe, and do not use their tails for clinging. All are active by day. Examples:

Goeldi's marmoset *Callimico goeldii* (8½ in., tail 12½ in.): found in the upper tributaries of the Amazon. It is black with a cape of long hair

Common marmoset *Callithrix jacchus*: found in the tropical and sub-tropical forests of Brazil and Bolivia

FAMILY CEBIDAE
Cebid monkeys; 26 species

These monkeys, which have nails on all their fingers and toes, are larger than marmosets, and tend to move less jerkily. Some species have prehensile tails. Examples:

Douroucouli or **night monkey** *Aotus trivirgatus* (18 in., tail 16 in.): the only nocturnal higher primate, it occurs in forests from Nicaragua to Argentina, and from the Guianas to Peru and Ecuador. It has large, owl-like eyes emphasised by the white areas around them

Spider monkey *Ateles paniscus*: found in the topmost branches in tropical forests from southern Mexico to Brazil. It has very long legs, and moves swiftly, using its tail as a fifth limb

FAMILY CERCOPITHECIDAE
Old World monkeys; 60 species

This is the first family of the catarrhine infra-order. Old World monkeys walk on all fours, have some facial expression, and the males have dagger-like canine teeth. The family includes two distinct groups: the colobines, with complex stomachs for feeding on leaves, and the omnivorous cercopithecines, which have simple stomachs and large cheek pouches in which food can be stored. Examples:

Black-and-white colobus *Colobus polykomos* (2 ft, tail 3 ft): found in the middle layers of the African forest. It has a coat of long glossy black hair with white markings

Sacred or **entellus langur** *Presbytis entellus*: colobine monkey found in the forests of India and Pakistan. Unlike other langurs, it lives mainly on the ground

Grivet, or **vervet monkey,** *Cercopithecus aethiops* (2 ft 8 in., tail 2 ft): lives in wooded savanna regions of Africa. It spends much of its time on the ground

Drill *Mandrillus leucophaeus* (2 ft 4 in., tail 5 in.): this forest-dwelling cercopithecine from western equatorial Africa has a black face, with prominent ridges on the sides of the nose, and red and blue buttocks

Gelada *Theropithecus gelada* (2 ft 5 in., tail 1 ft 8 in.): a cercopithecine found on the Ethiopian plateau. The gelada has a rounded muzzle, a bright red patch of naked skin on the chest, a long tufted tail and powerful jaws. The male has a mane

Rhesus monkey *Macaca mulatta* (24 in., tail 12 in.): a cercopithecine found in northern India, southern China and Indo-China. The Rh blood factor was first discovered in these monkeys

FAMILY PONGIDAE
Apes; 9 species

Like man and unlike other primates, apes have no tail, long arms and highly developed brains; they are man's closest living relatives. Examples:

Lar, or **common, gibbon** *Hylobates lar*: found in the rain forests of Burma, Thailand, Malaya, Borneo, Sumatra and Java. This slender, swift-moving animal lives almost entirely in the trees where it swings by its long arms from branch to branch; when on the ground it walks upright with its arms held high for balance. These gibbons live in pairs and make loud territorial calls

Orang-utan *Pongo pygmaeus* (up to 5 ft 6 in. tall): found in the forests of Borneo and northern Sumatra. The orang-utan has sparse, shaggy red hair and its hands and feet are similar to each other. The male has a huge goitre-like throat-sac and two fatty swellings in the cheeks

Gorilla *Gorilla gorilla* (up to 6 ft tall): found in the forests of equatorial Africa. Together with chimpanzees, gorillas, which are the largest living primates, are the animal species closest to man. The limbs are more human in proportion than those of the orang-utan, although the arms are longer than the legs. The feet are man-like, with the big toe larger than the others. Gorillas generally walk on all fours, arms supported by the backs of the middle part of the fingers, and are almost entirely ground-dwelling. They live in groups of up to 30 headed by an adult male, and are more quiet and retiring than chimpanzees. They have short dense black hair

Chimpanzee *Pan troglodytes* (about 3 ft 6 in.): found in the rain forests of tropical Africa; more widespread than the gorilla. Chimpanzees have large ears and long, scant black hair. They live in trees and on the ground in loose communities of up to 80, without fixed leaders

FAMILY HOMINIDAE
There is one species.

Man *Homo sapiens*: ranges throughout the world because of his ability to modify or create environments. The family evolved from ape-like ancestors about 26 million years ago, although modern man did not appear until about 40,000 years ago. Man is distinguished from other primates by his highly developed brain (enabling him to have a complex spoken language), his erect posture (involving considerable modification of the skeleton and muscles so that the body can be balanced on two legs), and sparse body hair

CLASSIFICATION

Mammals

PHYLUM CHORDATA	Animals with notochords
SUB-PHYLUM VERTEBRATA	Animals with backbones
CLASS MAMMALIA	Mammals
SUB-CLASS THERIA	Mammals that do not lay eggs
INFRA-CLASS EUTHERIA	Placental mammals
ORDER CETACEA	Whales

ORDER CETACEA

Whales

Cetaceans, the mammals most completely adapted to life in the water, have streamlined bodies tapering towards the tail. They cannot move about on land, their skin needs moisture continuously and, since they have no breastbone, most of them die if stranded on land because of the pressure on their lungs. Whales have no hind limbs. Their forelimbs are modified into broad flippers, and the tail has a horizontal fluke projecting on each side. A layer of blubber covers the whole body beneath the skin and helps to conserve heat. There are no external ears. The horizontal tail immediately distinguishes whales from fish. There are two distinct sub-orders of whales:

SUB-ORDER ODONTOCETI

Toothed whales

Generally much smaller than the whalebone whales, toothed whales have conical, pointed teeth in the lower or both jaws, or only one tusk-like tooth in the upper jaw. The lower jaw is narrow, not bowed outwards as in the baleen whales, and the tongue is small. Toothed whales feed mainly on fish. There are five families:

FAMILY PLATANISTIDAE

River dolphins; 4 species

All freshwater dolphins have long, almost bird-like beaks which may contain as many as 200 teeth. They live in the Amazon, Orinoco, Yangtse and Ganges rivers. Example:

Susu, or **Ganges dolphin** *Platanista gangetica*: lives in the Ganges, Brahmaputra and perhaps Indus rivers. It has tiny eyes but is blind and probes in the mud for shellfish

FAMILY ZIPHIIDAE

Beaked whales; 15 species

These medium-sized whales have a beak, one or two pairs of functional teeth in the lower jaw, and two to four throat furrows converging to form a V-pattern at the chin. Example:

Cuvier's beaked whale *Ziphius cavirostris*: found in all seas, but it is rare. It has only one pair of teeth

FAMILY PHYSETERIDAE

Sperm whales; 2 species

These whales have no dorsal fin and have functional teeth in the lower jaw, which is much shorter than the upper. The larger species has a barrel-shaped head, which is a third of the total body length and is filled with spermaceti oil, used in industry as a lubricant. It feeds mainly on squids. The pygmy sperm whale has a porpoise-like body. Example:

Sperm whale *Physeter catodon*: common in warm oceans; the males migrate to colder waters in summer

FAMILY MONODONTIDAE

White whales; 2 species

White whales are closely related to the dolphins but have fewer teeth and no dorsal fin. The species are:

Beluga, or **white whale,** *Delphinapterus leucas* (up to 18 ft): found in Arctic waters; it has 18 teeth in each jaw

Narwhal *Monodon monoceros*: found in Arctic waters. The male has teeth in the upper jaw, one (or rarely two) of which develops into a long twisted tusk, projecting forwards through the upper lip to a length of up to 8 ft; in the female these teeth remain undeveloped

FAMILY DELPHINIDAE

Dolphins and porpoises; 50 species

These mammals, generally small compared with other whales, have no throat grooves; they have teeth in both jaws, and most have a dorsal fin in the centre of the back. Examples:

Killer whale *Orcinus orca* (male up to 30 ft, female up to 15 ft): found in oceans throughout the world. This black-backed whale has a white underside, and a tall, narrow dorsal fin. Killer whales' stomachs have been found to contain dolphins up to 10 ft long

Atlantic bottle-nosed dolphin *Tursiops truncatus*: found in the North Atlantic and the Mediterranean Sea. It has a short snout with 20–26 teeth on each side of each jaw. Bottle-nosed dolphins, known as porpoises in North America, can be taught to give complex performances

Common or **harbour porpoise** *Phocaena phocaena* (up to 6 ft): found in the North Atlantic and adjacent seas; it commonly swims up rivers. It has no beak

SUB-ORDER MYSTICETI

Whalebone whales

Most species of whalebone whales are large—there is none less than 17 ft long when fully grown. There are no teeth in either jaw; instead, the V-shaped upper jaw has plates of baleen (whalebone), which act as sieves or strainers for plankton and are enclosed by the two halves of the lower jaw when the whale is not feeding. There are three families:

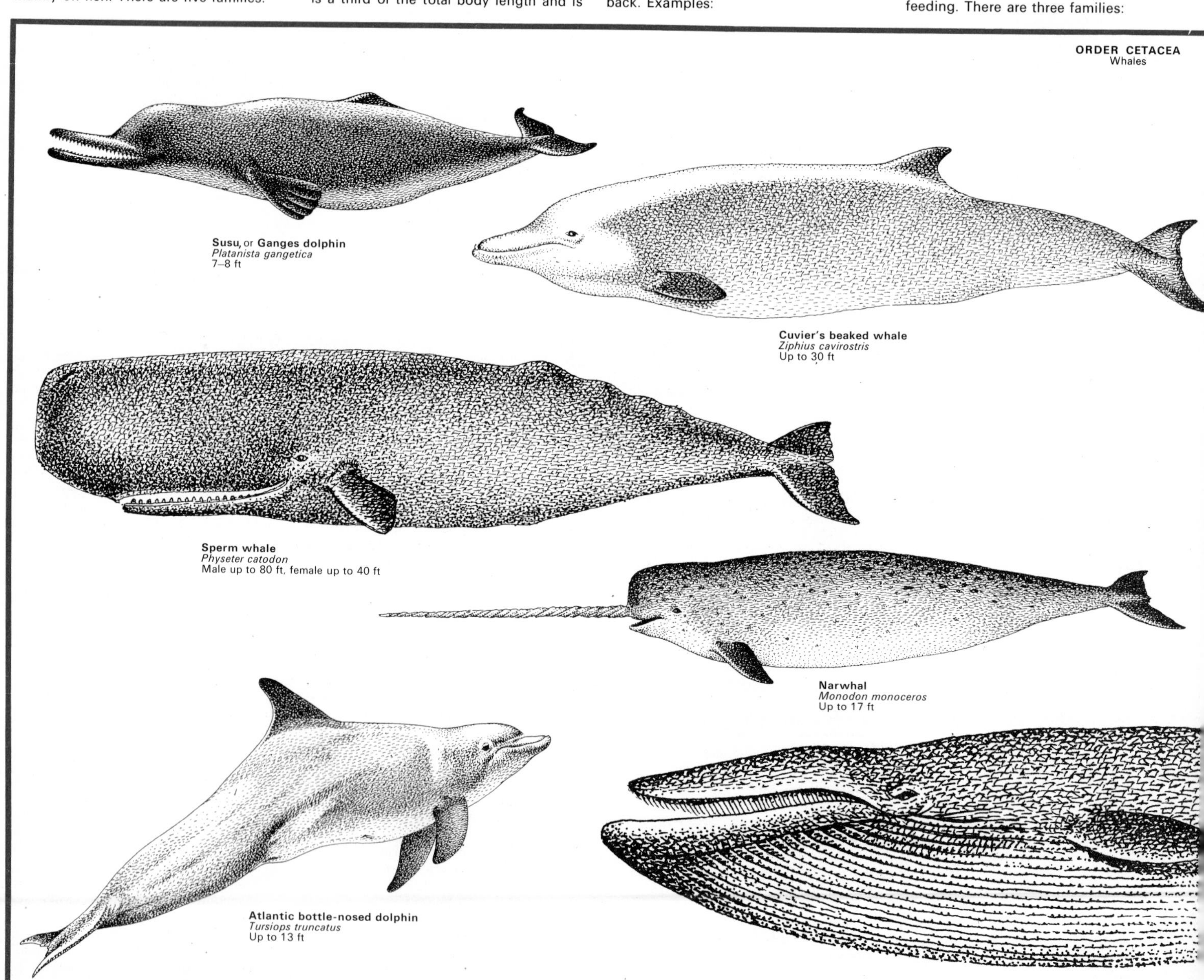

Susu, or **Ganges dolphin**
Platanista gangetica
7–8 ft

Cuvier's beaked whale
Ziphius cavirostris
Up to 30 ft

Sperm whale
Physeter catodon
Male up to 80 ft, female up to 40 ft

Narwhal
Monodon monoceros
Up to 17 ft

Atlantic bottle-nosed dolphin
Tursiops truncatus
Up to 13 ft

PHYLUM CHORDATA	Animals with notochords	INFRA-CLASS EUTHERIA	Placental mammals
SUB-PHYLUM VERTEBRATA	Animals with backbones	ORDER CETACEA	Whales
CLASS MAMMALIA	Mammals	ORDER EDENTATA	Anteaters, sloths and armadillos
SUB-CLASS THERIA	Mammals that do not lay eggs	ORDER PHOLIDOTA	Pangolins

FAMILY ESCHRICHTIIDAE

There is one species:

Californian grey whale *Eschrichtius gibbosus*: this whale migrates from Arctic waters to shallows off the Californian coast to breed. It has a very broad mouth, 2–4 ft deep furrows on the throat, and no dorsal fin but a series of low bumps on the back near the tail. The baleen is short and thick with coarsely frayed inner edges to strain the small bottom-living creatures on which this whale feeds

FAMILY BALAENOPTERIDAE

Rorquals; 6 species

Also called fin whales, the rorquals are distinguished from the right whales by a dorsal fin, narrow ridges on the throat, a smaller head (generally a quarter or a fifth of the body length), only slightly curved jaws, and shorter and less flexible baleen. Examples:

Blue whale *Balaenoptera musculus* (record length 108 ft): feeds in Arctic and Antarctic waters and migrates to subtropical waters to breed. It is the largest mammal that has ever lived

Common rorqual or **fin whale** *Balaenoptera physalus*: found in all oceans, feeding on herrings and cod as well as on plankton

FAMILY BALAENIDAE

Right whales; 3 species

These whales have long mouths—the head is more than a quarter of the total body length—and the lower jaw scoops down at the front so that it encloses the upper jaw only at the sides. There are no throat grooves and no dorsal fin. The baleen plates are long, narrow and very elastic, and these whales feed only on microscopic plankton. Example:

Greenland right whale *Balaena mysticetus*: found in the Arctic Ocean. It is black, except for a white chin and a grey area near the tail

ORDER EDENTATA

Anteaters, sloths and armadillos

These rather primitive New World mammals have on the forelimbs two or three fingers much longer than the others. These long fingers are used as hooks by sloths, to break open anthills by anteaters, and to burrow by armadillos. All lack front teeth, and cheek teeth, if present, have no enamel. There are three families:

FAMILY MYRMECOPHAGIDAE

Anteaters; 3 species

Anteaters have long, tapering snouts, tubular mouths with no teeth, and long sticky tongues. Example:

Tamandua or **lesser anteater** *Tamandua tetradactyla*: found in tropical forests from southern Mexico to Brazil. This tree-dwelling anteater has a non-bushy prehensile tail

FAMILY BRADYPODIDAE

Sloths; 5 species

The slow-moving tree sloths have short, rounded heads, inconspicuous ears, and forward-facing eyes. The hand has two or three fingers with which sloths suspend themselves upside-down from branches. The hairs hang downwards so that rain-water runs down to the back. Algae often grow on the surface of the straw-like hairs, giving the fur a green colour and camouflaging the animal among the leaves. Example:

Two-toed sloth *Choloepus didactylus*: lives in the forests of Venezuela, the Guianas and northern Brazil

FAMILY DASYPODIDAE

Armadillos; 20 species

Members of this family have a covering of horny plates or bands connected by flexible skin, so that most species can roll up into a ball for defence. They have three to five strong claws on the front feet which are used for burrowing, and up to 90 peg-like teeth. They roam in open country from the southern U.S.A. to the Argentine pampas. Example:

Nine-banded armadillo *Dasypus novemcinctus*: found in South and Central America, and in southern North America, where it is still extending its range. Its chief food includes insects and other invertebrates; it also eats birds' eggs

ORDER EDENTATA
Anteaters, sloths and armadillos

Tamandua or **lesser anteater**
Tamandua tetradactyla
24 in., tail 16 in.

Two-toed sloth
Choloepus didactylus
24 in.

Nine-banded armadillo
Dasypus novemcinctus
2 ft 6 in., tail 14½ in.

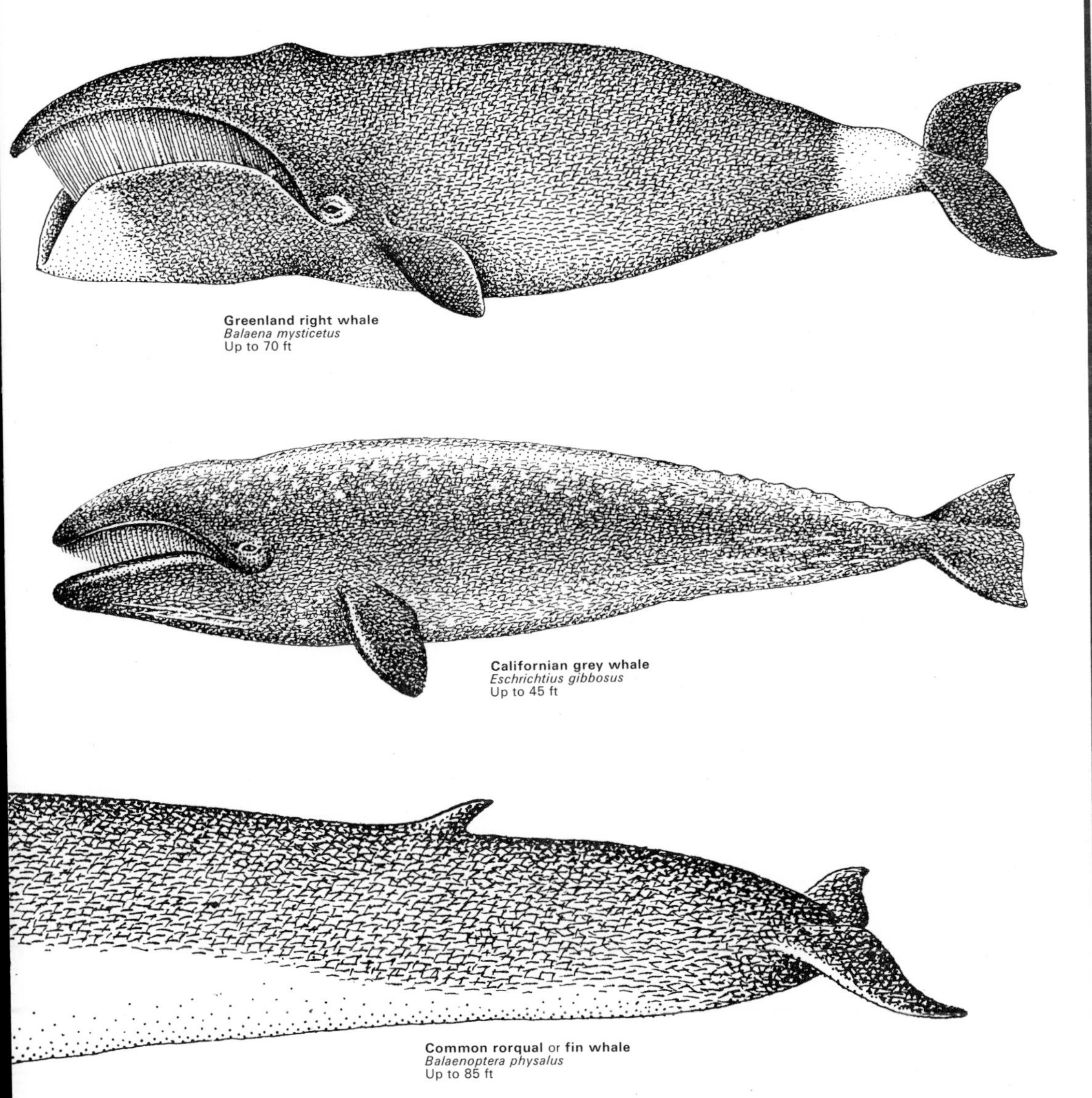

Greenland right whale
Balaena mysticetus
Up to 70 ft

Californian grey whale
Eschrichtius gibbosus
Up to 45 ft

Common rorqual or **fin whale**
Balaenoptera physalus
Up to 85 ft

ORDER PHOLIDOTA

The mammals of this order are the Old World counterparts of the New World edentates. There is only one family:

FAMILY MANIDAE

Pangolins; 7 species

This family, found in the Old World tropics, consists of animals with long tapering bodies, covered above with overlapping scales but with no scales on the snout, sides of the face or undersides. The tongue has muscular roots which pass down through the chest and attach to the pelvis; the five strong front claws are used to tear open termites' nests and for burrowing. Ground-dwelling species roll themselves into a ball for defence. Example:

Cape pangolin *Manis temminckii*: lives in dry savanna regions of southern and eastern Africa

Cape pangolin
Manis temminckii
24 in., tail 18 in.

Mammals

PHYLUM CHORDATA	Animals with notochords	INFRA-CLASS EUTHERIA	Placental mammals
SUB-PHYLUM VERTEBRATA	Animals with backbones	ORDER LAGOMORPHA	Pikas, hares and rabbits
CLASS MAMMALIA	Mammals	ORDER RODENTIA	Rodents
SUB-CLASS THERIA	Mammals that do not lay eggs		

ORDER LAGOMORPHA

Pikas, hares and rabbits

Although these animals resemble rodents, they have an additional pair of non-gnawing, chisel-shaped incisor teeth outside the normal pair. Their scrotum, unlike that of rodents, lies in front of the penis, which has no bone. They eat their feces the first time waste matter is passed from each meal, so making best use of plant food. There are two families:

FAMILY OCHOTONIDAE

Pikas or mouse hares; 14 species

Typical inhabitants of Arctic and alpine tundra, these animals are the most common small plant-eaters in Tibet and along the Siberian Arctic coast. They have short ears, no visible tail, long, dense, soft fur, and nostrils which can be closed in bad weather. The hind limbs are not very long, and the undersides of the feet are heavily furred. Example:

Rocky mountain pika *Ochotona princeps*: a pika found in the Rocky Mountains region of North America. Like other pikas, it dries grass in the sun and stores the hay as food for winter

FAMILY LEPORIDAE

Hares and rabbits; 50 species

The leporids are found throughout the world except in Australia, New Zealand, Madagascar and various oceanic islands (although some have been introduced to these places by man). They have short, furry, upturned tails and very long ears and hind limbs. They are most commonly active at dusk and dawn. Examples:

Brown hare *Lepus capensis*: a solitary animal, it rests in depressions in the ground among thick vegetation. Its powerful hind quarters and long back legs enable it to run at speeds of up to 40 mph

Eastern cottontail rabbit *Sylvilagus floridanus* (18 in.): lives in open or bushy country from southern Canada to Argentina, in old burrows of other animals

ORDER LAGOMORPHA
Pikas, hares and rabbits

Rocky mountain pika
Ochotona princeps
8 in.

Brown hare
Lepus capensis
24 in., tail 4 in.

ORDER RODENTIA

Rodents

Rodents are the most successful of modern mammals, apart from man, and are found in all parts of the world. They are easily identified by the long pair of chisel-like incisor teeth (with enamel on the front surface only) projecting from each jaw at the front of the mouth; these teeth grow continuously and if for any reason they are not worn down by gnawing, the tips may grow past each other and perforate the palate. In some rodents the lips can be closed behind the incisors so that the animals can gnaw without dirt entering their mouths. The scrotum, unlike that of the lagomorphs, is behind the penis, which has a bone. Three sub-orders are recognised on the basis of the position and structure of the jaw muscles:

SUB-ORDER SCIUROMORPHA

Squirrel-like rodents

This sub-order includes squirrels, marmots, gophers and beavers. There are seven families:

FAMILY APLODONTIDAE

There is one species:

Sewellel *Aplodontia rufa*: a thick-set, heavy, burrowing animal, often called the mountain beaver; it lives in forests, near streams, in western North America

FAMILY SCIURIDAE

Squirrels; 250 species

Found all over the world except Australia, squirrels are active during the day and generally live in trees, although some species are ground-dwelling and dig burrows. They have large eyes, and many are brightly coloured. Examples:

Eastern chipmunk *Tamias striatus*: found in deciduous forests and bush areas in the eastern U.S.A. and south-eastern Canada. It has black and yellow stripes down its back

Eurasian red squirrel *Sciurus vulgaris* (9 in., tail 7 in.): found in the coniferous forests of Europe and Asia; generally red-brown but sometimes black, it has conspicuous tufts on its ears

Alpine marmot *Marmota marmota* (20 in., tail 6 in.): this thick-set burrower lives in the Alps and Carpathians and is active during the day except from September to March when it hibernates

Red-and-white giant flying squirrel *Petaurista alborufa* (23 in., tail 25 in.): found in dense forests in southern Asia. This nocturnal animal lives in hollow trees during the day. A broad, furry gliding skin stretches from the wrist to the hind foot and to the base of the tail, enabling it to glide from tree to tree. It sometimes rides ascending air currents, and can bank and turn to control its glide

FAMILY GEOMYIDAE

Pocket gophers; 30 species

These North American burrowing rodents have strong digging claws and two long fur-lined external cheek pouches, used for carrying food, which the animal can turn inside-out for cleaning. They spend most of their lives underground. Example:

Plains pocket gopher *Geomys bursarius*: makes burrows up to 300 ft long in loose sandy soil in grasslands

FAMILY HETEROMYIDAE

Kangaroo rats and pocket mice; 70 species

Occurring from western North America to Venezuela, these animals have long hind limbs for jumping and cheek pouches like those of pocket gophers. They make burrows under bushes, and become torpid in cold weather. Example:

Merriam's kangaroo rat *Dipodomys merriami*: lives in arid areas of Mexico and western North America

FAMILY CASTORIDAE

There is one species:

Beaver *Castor fiber*: found in rivers and lakes in Europe, Asia and North America, the beaver is a water-dwelling rodent, with dense underfur overlaid with coarse guard hairs, ears and eyes which can be closed under water, webbed feet and a broad, paddle-shaped scaly tail. The dam-building activities of beavers can create large ponds and greatly change whole environments

FAMILY ANOMALURIDAE

Scaly-tailed squirrels; 9 species

Except for members of the genus *Zenkerella*, all scaly-tailed squirrels have a gliding skin or membrane between the limbs, extending to the tail. All scaly-tailed squirrels have two overlapping rows of scales on the underside of the tail which act as an 'anti-skid' device when they land on a tree-trunk. Example:

Pel's scaly-tailed squirrel *Anomalurus peli*: found in forests of West Africa

FAMILY PEDETIDAE

There is one species:

Springhaas, or **Cape jumping hare**, *Pedetes capensis*: lives in grasslands and open bush in eastern and southern Africa. Except for the bushy tail, the springhaas has a kangaroo-like appearance with long hind legs and ears, and a soft coat

SUB-ORDER MYOMORPHA

Mouse-like rodents

This large group contains more than 1000 species of rodents. There are nine families:

FAMILY CRICETIDAE

Hamsters and allies; 570 species

Most members of this family burrow. Many have thick-set bodies and short tails and legs. Examples:

White-footed deer mouse *Peromyscus leucopus* (4 in., tail 4 in.): extremely abundant in North and Central America. This rodent bears a striking resemblance in form, colour and habits to the European long-tailed field-mouse of the family Muridae. It has a soft, sandy-coloured coat, large ears, and a hairy tail as long as its body

Eastern wood rat *Neotoma floridana* (9 in., tail 8 in.): found in eastern North America. The wood rat makes a nest of twigs, rocks and bones, and picks up anything attractive—often a piece of silver paper—as nest material, a habit which has given it and its relatives the alternative names 'trade rat' and 'pack rat'

Common hamster *Cricetus cricetus* (10 in., tail 2 in.): found in the steppes of Europe and Asia and in ploughed land and along river banks. It has cheek pouches and broad feet with well-developed claws for burrowing

Brown lemming *Lemmus lemmus* (5 in., tail 1 in.): lives in tundra of Europe, Asia and North America. It is a heavily furred, stocky rodent with very short ears and tail. Lemmings burrow through the soil in summer and under the snow in winter; they make nests of grass and moss. Every 4–5 years, when the population cycle is at its peak and there are too many animals for the food available, they migrate in vast numbers in search of new territories

Musk rat or **musquash** *Ondatra zibethicus* (13 in., tail 10 in.): lives in marshes, lakes and rivers of North America and has been introduced into Europe. Its hind feet are partly webbed with a fringe of hairs, called the swimming fringe, along the edges; its tail is flattened. The musk rat builds mounds in swamps, connected with the land by long tunnels with underwater exits

Round-tailed musk rat *Neofiber alleni*: found in bogs and swamps in Florida and southern Georgia. It is a good swimmer and burrower, building mounds in moist soil. Its fur has long guard hairs and soft, short underfur

Sewellel
Aplodontia rufa
17 in., tail 1 in.

Merriam's kangaroo rat
Dipodomys merriami
4 in., tail 6 in.

Beaver
Castor fiber
3 ft, tail 12 in.

Eastern chipmunk
Tamias striatus
6 in., tail 4 in.

Pel's scaly-tailed squirrel
Anomalurus peli
17 in., tail 18 in.

Plains pocket gopher
Geomys bursarius
9 in., tail 4 in.

Springhaas or
Cape jumping
Pedetes capens
24 in., tail 21 in

SUB-PHYLUM VERTEBRATA	Animals with backbones
CLASS MAMMALIA	Mammals
SUB-CLASS THERIA	Mammals that do not lay eggs
INFRA-CLASS EUTHERIA	Placental mammals
ORDER RODENTIA	Rodents

Short-tailed vole *Microtus agrestris* (4 in., tail $1\frac{1}{2}$ in.): found in moist meadows, moors and open woods in Europe and western Asia. The long loose fur nearly hides the short ears. It digs surface runways and sometimes shallow burrows

Lesser Egyptian gerbil *Gerbillus gerbillus* (4 in., tail 3 in.): a common desert rodent, ranging from Palestine southwards to Uganda and as far west as Nigeria. It has a sandy coat with white feet and underparts

FAMILY SPALACIDAE
Mediterranean mole-rats; 3 species

These rodents have long bodies; short legs; soft, dense, reversible fur; tactile bristles on the snout; no external eye openings and no external ears. They are found in eastern Europe and south-western Asia. Example:

Greater mole-rat *Spalax microphthalmus*: found in steppes of southern Russia; it is an extensive burrower

FAMILY RHIZOMYIDAE
Bamboo rats and African mole-rats; 18 species

With their compact bodies adapted for burrowing and their long incisor teeth uncovered by the lips, these rats resemble the American pocket gophers, except that they have no cheek pouches. Bamboo rats live in southern Asia. Example:

Splendid mole-rat *Tachyoryctes splendens*: found in Ethiopia

FAMILY MURIDAE
Old World rats and mice; 500 species

Most of the rats and mice in this family are small animals with naked, scaly tails and long snouts. The structure of their teeth distinguishes them from the Cricetidae. Examples:

Black rat *Rattus rattus* (9 in., tail 10 in.): probably originated in south-eastern Asia, but is now found throughout the world in association with man. It is host to a flea which carries a bacterium causing plague, and is active mainly at night

House mouse *Mus musculus*: originated in the dry areas of Europe and Asia but is now common throughout the world, living in association with man in town and country; it is active mainly by night

Striped grass mouse *Lemniscomys striatus* (5 in., tail $5\frac{1}{2}$ in.): found in various open habitats in Africa, this mouse has buff stripes on a dark brown background. It is a ground-dwelling rodent, active during the day

Giant pouched rat *Cricetomys gambianus* (15 in., tail 18 in.): this nocturnal African rat has short, thin fur, big ears, a long narrow head, cheek pouches, and a white tail-tip. It is unique in carrying parasitic cockroaches

FAMILY GLIRIDAE
Dormice; 10 species

Dormice, found in Europe, Asia and Africa, have rather bushy tails, soft coats, short bodies, short legs and toes, and curved claws for climbing. In the northern part of their range they become fat in autumn and are dormant from October to April. Example:

Hazel dormouse *Muscardinus avellanarius*: ranges from Britain to Asia Minor and Russia. It lives in dense undergrowth, hiding by day in a nest of vegetation built in the lower branches of trees

FAMILY PLATACANTHOMYIDAE
Spiny dormouse and Chinese pygmy dormouse; 2 species

These Asian rodents look like dormice except that the tail is scaly at the base and ends in a brush. They have large ears and long hind feet. Example:

Spiny dormouse *Platacanthomys lasiurus*: found in southern India. This rodent lives in trees and is found mainly in rocky hill country

FAMILY SELEVINIIDAE
There is one species:

Desert dormouse *Selevinia betpakdalaensis*: a rare animal discovered in 1938 in the clay and sandy deserts of Kazakhstan, in the Soviet Union. It has a round body and long, non-bushy tail. It moults in an unusual way: the hair comes off in patches, along with the skin

FAMILY ZAPODIDAE
Birch mice and jumping mice; 11 species

These small, mouse-like animals are found in forests, meadows and swamps in northern Europe, Asia and North America. They have internal cheek pouches, long hind legs used for jumping and a long tail for balancing. Example:

Meadow jumping mouse *Zapus hudsonius*: inhabits meadows in the forested areas of North America

FAMILY DIPODIDAE
Jerboas; 25 species

These animals, found in Asia and northern Africa, are remarkably well adapted for jumping, with hind legs at least four times as long as the front legs, elongated feet with three central bones fused to form a single bone for strength and support, and long tails. Example:

Four-toed jerboa *Allactaga tetradactyla*: found only in Egypt, it burrows in sandy soils. It is the only jerboa with four toes on the hind feet

SUB-ORDER HYSTRICOMORPHA
Porcupine-like rodents

The 16 families in this sub-order of rodents range from the spine-bearing porcupines to the guinea-pigs and coypus

FAMILY HYSTRICIDAE
Old World porcupines; 20 species

These large, thick-set, short-legged rodents from Africa, Italy and southern Asia have long, sharp quills for defence in addition to hair on their bodies and tails. Example:

Indian crested porcupine *Hystrix indica*: lives in forests, rocky hills and ravines. It spends most of the day in its burrow and emerges at night to feed

FAMILY ERETHIZONTIDAE
New World porcupines; 23 species

These porcupines have shorter spines than their Old World counterparts; some of the spines are barbed. Their feet are modified for life in the trees—the sole is widened and the first toe on the hind foot is replaced by a broad, movable pad. Example:

North American porcupine *Erethizon dorsatum*: inhabits timbered regions of Alaska and other western states of the U.S.A., and Canada

FAMILY CAVIIDAE
Cavies or guinea-pigs; 23 species

Members of this South American family are found in rocky areas, savannas, forest edges and swamps. They have fairly coarse coats, large heads, long, thin limbs and rudimentary tails. Example:

Wild guinea-pig *Cavia tschudi*: digs its own burrows or occupies the deserted burrows of other animals

FAMILY HYDROCHOERIDAE
There is one species:

Capybara *Hydrochoerus hydrochaeris*: the largest living rodent. The capybara is semi-aquatic, living in groups by rivers and lakes in Central and South America. It has a broad head, short, rounded ears and webbed feet. There is a bare raised gland on the top of the snout in the adult male

FAMILY DINOMYIDAE
There is one species:

Pacarana *Dinomys branickii*: found in forests on the lower slopes of the Andes. It is thick-set, with a short stout furry tail, short ears and limbs, and long claws and whiskers

FAMILY DASYPROCTIDAE
Agoutis, acuchis and pacas; 30 species

Members of this family have long legs, small, thick, hoof-like claws, and a coarse thick coat. Example:

Red-rumped agouti *Dasyprocta aguti*: found in forests in Brazil and the Guianas

FAMILY CHINCHILLIDAE

Chinchillas and viscachas; 6 species

Most chinchillas are found in the foothills of the southern Andes. They have a large head, broad snout, large eyes and ears, and a long, fine coat. Their hind limbs are adapted for jumping, but they run, leap or creep on all fours. Example:

Chinchilla *Chinchilla laniger*: lives in barren, rocky mountain areas of Chile and Bolivia. It is farmed for its dense, silky, blue to pearl-grey fur

FAMILY CAPROMYIDAE

Coypus and hutias; 10 species

A family of robust, often aquatic, rodents; its members have small ears and eyes, short limbs, prominent claws, and a sparsely haired tail. Example:

Coypu *Myocastor coypus*: native to the streams and lakes of South America, but is farmed in Europe for its soft velvety fur, called nutria. It is active by day. All other species of capromyids are found in the West Indies

FAMILY OCTODONTIDAE

Octodonts; 8 species

These rat-like animals have long, silky body fur and coarsely haired tails which some species carry erect when running. They are found in South America from coastal regions up to 10,000 ft, and live in burrows. Example:

Degu *Octodon degus*: found in mountains of Peru and Chile

FAMILY CTENOMYIDAE

Tuco-tucos; 26 species

Tuco-tucos resemble pocket gophers but have no cheek pouches. They make their burrows in dry, sandy soil. Example:

Ctenomys peruanus: lives in South America

FAMILY ABROCOMIDAE

Chinchilla rats; 2 species

These rodents, which have long, dense underfur with fine guard hairs, are rat-like in appearance, with large eyes and ears, finely haired tails, short limbs, and weak claws which are hollow underneath. They live in crevices and burrows. Example:

Bennett's chinchilla rat *Abrocoma bennetti*: lives in the Andes and on the coastal hills of Chile

FAMILY ECHIMYIDAE

Spiny rats; 75 species

Rat-like in general appearance, these rodents of Central and South America generally have bristly fur. Example:

Guira *Euryzygomatomys spinosus*: found in Brazil and Paraguay in grassy and bushy areas

FAMILY THRYONOMYIDAE

Cane rats; 6 species

These rodents, widespread in Africa, have bristly hairs, flattened and grooved along their upper surfaces, growing in groups of five or six. Example:

Cutting grass *Thryonomys swinderianus*: inhabits reed beds and long grass

FAMILY PETROMYIDAE

There is one species:

Rock rat *Petromus typicus*: a squirrel-like rodent from south-western Africa. It has flexible ribs which enable it to squeeze through narrow crevices

FAMILY BATHYERGIDAE

African mole-rats; 50 species

Like other burrowing mammals, mole-rats have stocky bodies, strong feet, short tails and limbs, and small eyes and ears. Example:

Cape mole-rat *Georychus capensis*: lives in southern Africa in areas with loose, sandy soil

FAMILY CTENODACTYLIDAE

Gundis and Speke's pectinator; 8 species

The gundis of northern Africa look like guinea-pigs. They have soft fur, and comb-like brushes of bristles on two digits of the hind feet, for cleaning fur. Example:

Lataste's gundi *Massoutiera mzabi*: a gundi found in the western and central Sahara

ORDER CARNIVORA

Flesh-eating mammals

Most carnivores are well equipped for meat-eating, with powerful jaws, large canine teeth, cheek teeth used for shearing and crushing, and strong claws for gripping. Most have agile, graceful bodies; but some, like the almost omnivorous bears, are more heavily built. Carnivores are divided into two sub-orders, depending on the structure of the bones of the skull surrounding the middle and inner parts of the ear:

SUB-ORDER AELUROIDEA

Cats, hyenas and civets

This sub-order of generally cat-like mammals contains three families:

FAMILY FELIDAE

Cats; 34 species

Almost exclusively meat-eating, the cats are lightly built, with five digits on the front feet and four on the rear; almost all have strongly curved, retractile claws. They stalk their prey or lie in wait and spring on it with a short rush. Examples:

Cheetah *Acinonyx jubatus* (4 ft 6 in., tail 2 ft 6 in.): a swift-running, leanly built cat with non-retractile claws, found on the plains of Africa and south-western Asia

Wild cat *Felis silvestris* (2 ft 6 in., tail 14 in.): found wild in Europe, western Asia and Africa, it is the ancestor of the domestic cat

Lion *Panthera leo*: lives in the grasslands of Africa and south-western Asia, where it is now rare. Tawny yellow in colour, it hunts large grazing animals of the savanna, especially zebras and wildebeeste. The male has a ruff of hair—the mane—round the shoulders and neck

FAMILY HYAENIDAE

Hyenas and aardwolf; 4 species

Hyenas look rather like dogs, but their hindquarters are proportionally lower and less muscular. All have long limbs and large ears. Examples:

Spotted or **laughing hyena** *Crocuta crocuta*: lives on the African plains. It is a scavenger, especially on the remains of lions' prey, and a predator on wildebeeste, gazelles and zebras, among others. During the breeding season and when excited, it produces a characteristic laughing cry. It has four toes on the front feet

Aardwolf *Proteles cristatus* (2 ft 6 in., tail 10 in.): this small, striped animal with long, crest-like hair on its back is found on the savannas of southern and eastern Africa. It has very small teeth (unlike hyenas), and feeds almost entirely on termites and other insects. There are five toes on the front feet

FAMILY VIVERRIDAE

Civets and allies; about 75 species

These small and medium-sized carnivores of the warmer parts of the Old World have long, low bodies, short legs, long—generally bushy—tails, and pointed snouts. There are five toes on the front feet. Most of them are active at night. Nearly all have scent glands. Examples:

African civet *Civettictis civetta* (2 ft 6 in., tail 18 in.): found in forests and savanna; it has glands under the tail which produce a pungent oily secretion used in making perfume

Blotched genet *Genetta tigrina*: found in forests and thick grass in Africa. Genets have fine fur and are more clearly marked than civets

Binturong *Arctitis binturong* (3 ft, tail 2 ft 6 in.): a stockily built animal with a shaggy black coat, it can be distinguished from other members of its family by its long ear-tufts and bushy, prehensile tail. It feeds mainly on plants and lives in tropical forests in south-eastern Asia

Egyptian mongoose *Herpestes ichneumon* (24 in., tail 20 in.): this day-active animal lives in thick vegetation by rivers in African savanna. It was a sacred animal in ancient Egypt

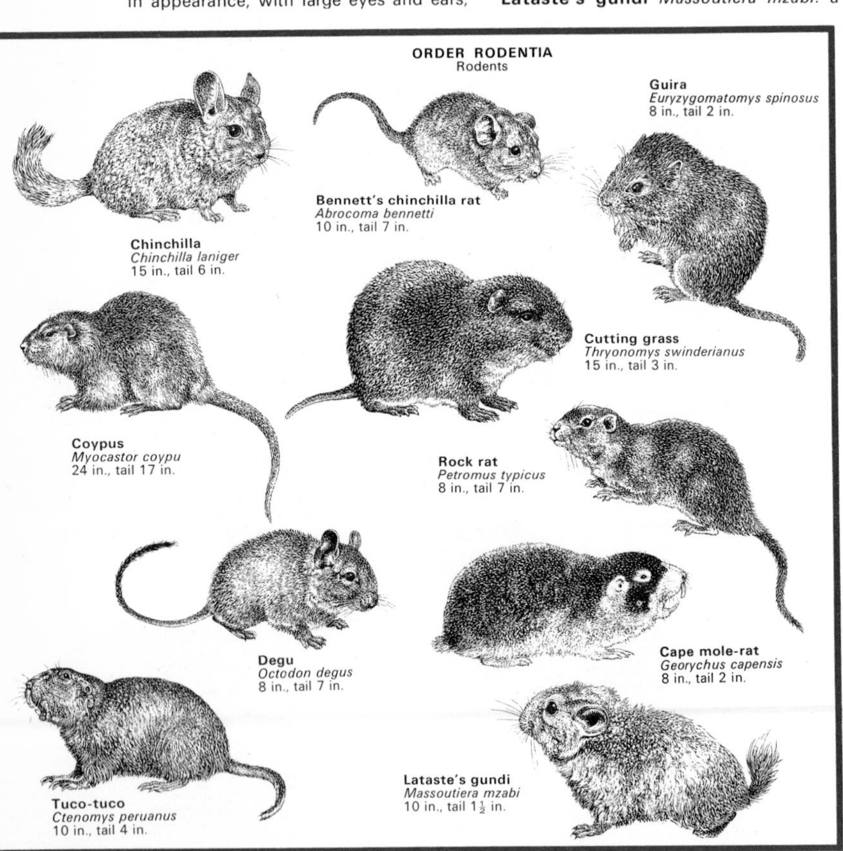

PHYLUM CHORDATA	Animals with notochords	INFRA-CLASS EUTHERIA	Placental mammals
SUB-PHYLUM VERTEBRATA	Animals with backbones	ORDER CARNIVORA	Flesh-eating mammals
CLASS MAMMALIA	Mammals	ORDER PINNIPEDIA	Seals, sea lions and walrus
SUB-CLASS THERIA	Mammals that do not lay eggs	ORDER PROBOSCIDEA	Elephants

SUB-ORDER ARCTOIDEA

Dogs, weasels, bears and raccoons
This sub-order of carnivores contains all the dog-like and bear-like mammals. There are four families:

FAMILY CANIDAE

Dogs; 37 species
These animals with long, slender limbs and bushy tails are generally good runners, moving on the tips of their toes. They have keen hearing and sight, but hunt mainly by scent and often run in packs of about 30. They can be divided broadly into dog-like and fox-like types. All have four toes on the front feet. Examples:
Black-backed jackal *Canis mesomelas*: found in eastern and southern Africa, it can run at about 35 mph, and is a pest in southern Africa
Cape hunting dog *Lycaon pictus* (3 ft 6 in., tail 16 in.): these dogs of the African plains range widely in packs, preying on any animals they can overpower
Fennec *Fennecus zerda* (16 in., tail 12 in.): this big-eared fox inhabits desert regions of northern Africa, living in burrows in the sand

FAMILY MUSTELIDAE

Weasels and their allies; about 70 species
Most mustelids are small animals; they have long, slender bodies and long tails. They walk on the soles of the feet rather than on the tips of the toes as dogs do. There are five digits on both the front and hind feet. Examples:
American mink *Mustela vison*: found in Canada and the U.S.A., it has dark brown fur adapted for an aquatic life, and yields the mink pelts highly valued by the fur trade. It nests in holes in banks, rocks and debris
Striped skunk *Mephitis mephitis* (18 in., tail 10 in.): found in North America. Two scent glands at the base of the tail contain a foul-smelling fluid which the animal can squirt at an aggressor up to distances of 10 ft
European badger *Meles meles* (2 ft 6 in., tail 8 in.): also found in Asia in grassland and wooded areas. This omnivorous mammal is active at night
Eurasian otter *Lutra lutra* (2 ft 6 in., tail 20 in.): this freshwater mammal has webbed feet and a tail thickened at the base
Pine marten *Martes martes* (24 in., tail 12 in.): found in wooded regions in northern Europe and western Asia, where it hunts small mammals and birds

FAMILY URSIDAE

Bears; 7 species
Except for the polar bear, which feeds mainly on seals, bears are omnivorous. They are the largest carnivores, and are heavily built with short, powerful legs and short tails, and they walk on the soles of their feet. Example:
Brown bear *Ursus arctos*: found in North America, Europe and Asia. The species is in danger of extinction in the western parts of the U.S.A. and its numbers in Europe have been greatly reduced

FAMILY PROCYONIDAE

Raccoons and pandas; 18 species
Raccoons are found in the Americas, and pandas in Asia. All closely resemble bears but are smaller, and they have two molar teeth instead of the bears' three on each side of the lower jaw. Examples:
Giant panda *Ailuropoda melanoleuca* (5 ft, tail 5 in.): a day-active panda found in a restricted region of Szechwan, China, on the slopes of the Tibetan plateau, feeding mainly on bamboo. It looks like a bear, but is almost certainly more closely related to the raccoons
Raccoon *Procyon lotor* (24 in., tail 12 in.): found in North and Central America. A nocturnal animal, it feeds on fruit, seeds, insects and crayfish which it crushes with its strong, back teeth
South American coati *Nasua nasua*: a day-active animal generally found in forest regions in groups of 6–40. It has a long, mobile snout

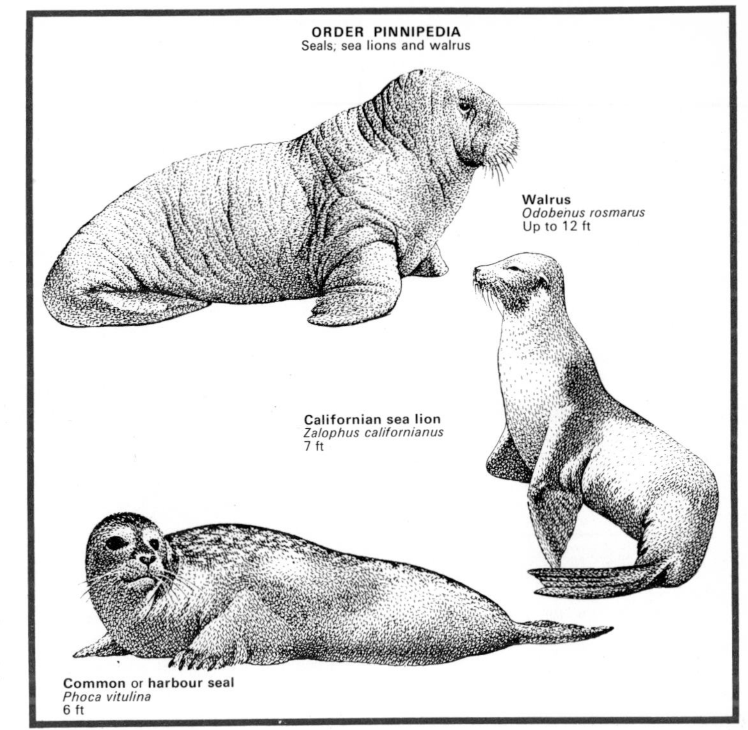

ORDER PINNIPEDIA

Seals, sea lions and walrus
Pinnipeds are flesh-eating mammals with streamlined, torpedo-shaped bodies, limbs modified into flippers, and webbed feet—adaptations for life in the water. A thick layer of oily fat, or blubber, under the skin insulates them against the cold. They are closely related to the carnivores, from which they probably evolved about 30 million years ago. There are three families:

FAMILY ODOBENIDAE

There is one species:
Walrus *Odobenus rosmarus*: found in Arctic waters. Like the eared seals, the walrus can turn its hind flippers forwards to aid movement on land; but unlike them it has no external ears. The upper canines of the adult male grow downwards to form tusks up to 27 in. long

FAMILY OTARIIDAE

Sea lions or eared seals; 13 species
Unlike the walrus, the eared seals have conspicuous external ears; they can use all four limbs when moving on land. The family is divided into two groups, sea lions and fur seals. Examples:
Californian sea lion *Zalophus californianus*: found on the south-western coast of North America. It is the most abundant species, and the one commonly seen in zoos
Northern fur seal *Callorhinus ursinus* (7 ft): migrates in winter from the Bering Sea to California and Japan

FAMILY PHOCIDAE

Earless or true seals; 18 species
The true seals, which may have evolved from the same stock as did the otter (other pinnipeds may have evolved from a bear-like ancestor), have no obvious external ears, and their hind limbs or flippers cannot be swung forwards for moving on land. Examples:
Common or **harbour seal** *Phoca vitulina*: generally found on shores with sandbanks in the Northern Hemisphere
Southern Elephant seal *Mirounga leonina* (up to 20 ft): found in sub-Antarctic waters. The largest of all pinnipeds, it weighs up to 4 tons

ORDER PROBOSCIDEA

There is one family

FAMILY ELEPHANTIDAE

Elephants; 2 species
The elephant's most conspicuous external feature is its long flexible trunk, which is an elongation of the nose. The animal rests its weight on a fatty cushion beneath each of its broad feet. The single pair of upper incisors grow into large ivory tusks, and the cheek teeth replace each other throughout life
Asiatic elephant *Elephas maximus* (up to 10 ft tall at the shoulder): found in the tropical forests of southern Asia. This elephant has a flat forehead and small ears. Only the male has tusks, which may grow to 7 ft long
African elephant *Loxodonta africana*: found throughout Africa south of the Sahara. It is distinguished from the Asiatic elephant by its arched forehead, large ears, and two finger-like 'lips' at the end of the trunk. Males weigh up to $6\frac{1}{2}$ tons. Both sexes have tusks, which may grow to 11 ft long in the male and weigh more than 200 lb. each

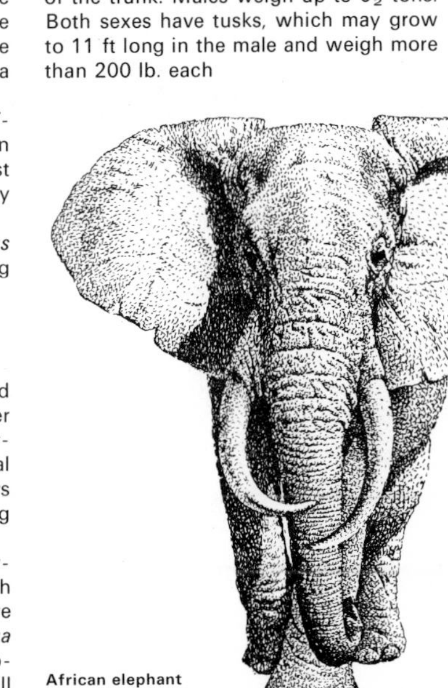

Mammals

PHYLUM CHORDATA	Animals with notochords	ORDER HYRACOIDEA	Hyraxes
SUB-PHYLUM VERTEBRATA	Animals with backbones	ORDER SIRENIA	Sea-cows
CLASS MAMMALIA	Mammals	ORDER TUBULIDENTATA	Aardvark
SUB-CLASS THERIA	Mammals that do not lay eggs	ORDER PERISSODACTYLA	Odd-toed hoofed mammals
INFRA-CLASS EUTHERIA	Placental mammals	ORDER ARTIODACTYLA	Even-toed hoofed mammals

ORDER HYRACOIDEA

There is one family:

FAMILY PROCAVIIDAE

Hyraxes or dassies; 6 species
Sometimes mistaken for rabbits, hyraxes are very distantly related to elephants. They have a short snout, short ears, short, sturdy legs, and the toes bear flattened, hoof-like nails. Example:
Rock hyrax *Procavia capensis*: frequents rocky regions in Africa and the Near East. It makes a high whistling sound when alarmed

Rock hyrax
Procavia capensis
22 in.

ORDER SIRENIA

Sea-cows
These animals are distantly related to elephants and hyraxes, but are entirely adapted for life in the water, with a massive, cigar-shaped body, paddle-like forelimbs, no hind limbs, and a flattened tail. These slow-moving, plant-eating mammals are found in estuaries or near the coast. They either are solitary or associate in groups of up to six. There are two families:

FAMILY TRICHECHIDAE

Manatees; 3 species
Manatees have scattered hairs on their bodies. The upper lip is deeply split, each half moving independently, and the tail fin is rounded. Adults do not have incisor teeth. Example:
North American manatee *Trichechus manatus*: found along the coasts of Florida, Central America and the West Indian islands

FAMILY DUGONGIDAE

There is one species:
Dugong *Dugong dugon*: frequents the warm shores of the western Pacific and Indian Oceans. Dugongs have a deeply notched tail fin and no hair on their bodies. A pair of incisor teeth form tusks in the male

ORDER TUBULIDENTATA

There is one family:

FAMILY ORYCTEROPODIDAE

There is one species:
Aardvark *Orycteropus afer*: widespread in African grasslands. It has long ears, an elongated muzzle ending in wide nostrils, and a long, heavy tail. The tubular mouth contains a long, sticky tongue with which the animal picks up ants and termites; it has powerful claws, used for burrowing

Aardvark
Orycteropus afer
2 ft 6 in., tail 24 in.

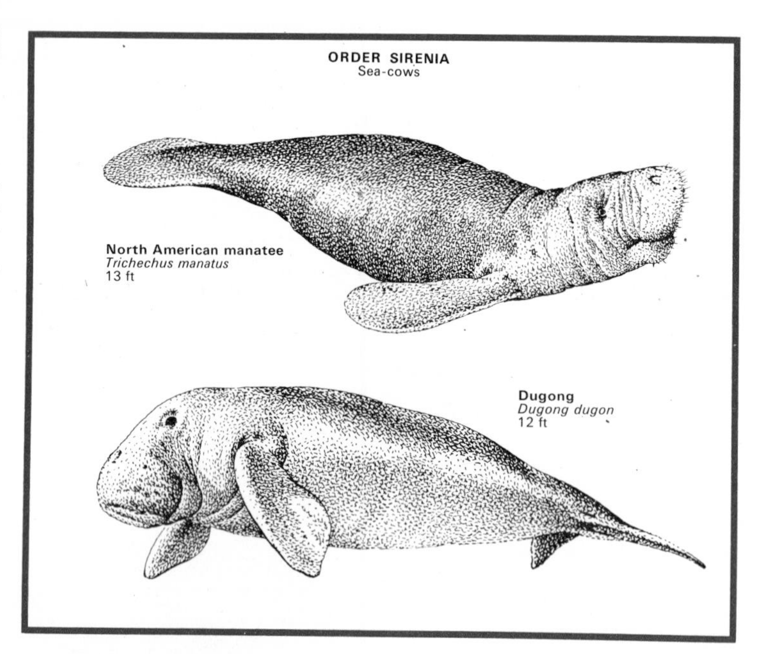

ORDER SIRENIA
Sea-cows

North American manatee
Trichechus manatus
13 ft

Dugong
Dugong dugon
12 ft

ORDER PERISSODACTYLA

Odd-toed hoofed mammals
These medium-sized to large animals, many of which are good runners, commonly have a reduced number of toes, each encased in a protective horny sheath, or hoof, and the weight is carried mainly by the middle digit of each foot. All are plant-eaters; their lips and incisor teeth are adapted for plucking plants, and their cheek-teeth for chewing. There are two sub-orders of odd-toed ungulates:

SUB-ORDER CERATOMORPHA

Tapirs and rhinoceroses
These stoutly built animals are found today only in the tropics and sub-tropics. There are two families:

FAMILY TAPIRIDAE

Tapirs; 4 species
Tapirs are heavy-bodied browsing animals which live near water in forests in Central and South America and south-east Asia. A flexible proboscis overhangs the upper lip, and they have four toes on the front feet and three on the hind feet. Example:
Malayan tapir *Tapirus indicus*: found from Thailand to Sumatra, it has a striking black-and-white coat which probably acts as disruptive camouflage

FAMILY RHINOCEROTIDAE

Rhinoceroses; 5 species
Rhinoceroses, though heavily built and thick-skinned, can move swiftly over short distances. They have one or two fibrous horns on the nose, often a protruding upper lip, and three toes on all feet. They live in African grasslands and in the forests of southern Asia. Example:
Black rhinoceros *Diceros bicornis*: found from southern and eastern Africa westwards to northern Nigeria. It lives alone or in pairs, and has two horns, the larger front horn growing up to 3 ft long

SUB-ORDER HIPPOMORPHA

This sub-order, which contains the horses and extinct titanotheres, differs from the other sub-order of perissodactyls mainly in the structure of the teeth. There is only one family:

FAMILY EQUIDAE

Horses, asses and zebras; 6 species
All horses are swift runners with only one functional toe on each foot. They live in herds. The cheek-teeth are adapted for grinding plant food. Examples:
Przewalski's horse *Equus caballus przewalskii* (4 ft 6 in. at the shoulder): found in Mongolia, it is the only surviving race of the species from which domestic horses are descended
African wild ass *Equus asinus*: this wild ancestor of the donkey is found in the deserts of northern Africa

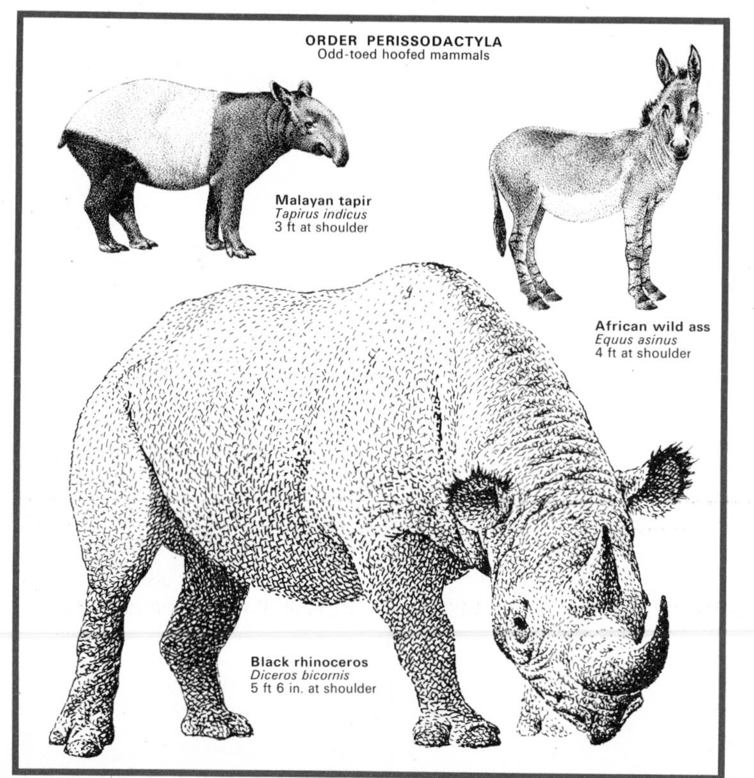

ORDER PERISSODACTYLA
Odd-toed hoofed mammals

Malayan tapir
Tapirus indicus
3 ft at shoulder

African wild ass
Equus asinus
4 ft at shoulder

Black rhinoceros
Diceros bicornis
5 ft 6 in. at shoulder

ORDER ARTIODACTYLA

Even-toed hoofed mammals
One of the most numerous groups of mammals today, the even-toed ungulates rest their weight equally on the third and fourth toes of each foot and have an even number of functional toes. There are three sub-orders:

SUB-ORDER SUIFORMES

This group of primitive even-toed hoofed mammals do not chew the cud. There are three families:

FAMILY SUIDAE

Pigs; 8 species
Pigs have a stocky body with a long head and mobile snout used for rooting, and sparse, bristly hair. They have a simple stomach, and eat both plant and animal food. Both their upper and lower tusk-like canine teeth point upwards. There are four toes on each foot, but the two central toes are the largest. Example:
Wild boar *Sus scrofa*: found in woodlands in Europe, northern Africa and nearly the whole of Asia, it is the ancestor of the domestic pig and has large powerful tusks

FAMILY TAYASSUIDAE

Peccaries; 2 species
Gregarious pig-like mammals from Central and South America, peccaries also have some ruminant characteristics: a fairly complex stomach, united third and fourth foot bones (these are separate in pigs), and tusk-like canines that point downwards and not upwards as in pigs. Example:
Collared peccary *Tayassu tajacu*: found in open forest and along forest edges in South and Central America and in the southern U.S.A.

FAMILY HIPPOPOTAMIDAE

Hippopotamuses; 2 species
These animals are good swimmers and divers. Their large, heavy, short-legged bodies have a thick layer of fat under the skin, and their slightly webbed feet have four toes. The bulls fight, using their tusk-like lower canines as weapons. Examples:
Common hippopotamus *Hippopotamus amphibius*: found in most African rivers; weighs 4 tons
Pygmy hippopotamus *Choeropsis liberiensis* (2 ft tall at the shoulder): found in forests near water in western Africa

SUB-ORDER TYLOPODA

The animals forming this sub-order have complex stomachs and chew the cud, but have been separate from the ruminant sub-order for about 55 million years. There is one family:

FAMILY CAMELIDAE
Camels; 3 wild species
Camels and llamas have only two functional toes, supported by expanded pads for walking on sand or snow. The slender snout bears a cleft upper lip. Examples:
Bactrian camel *Camelus bactrianus*: found wild in the Gobi Desert and introduced elsewhere, it has two humps and shaggy hair
Guanaco *Lama guanicoe* (4 ft tall at the shoulder): found from sea level to 15,000 ft in the Andes and in central and south-eastern South America. It may be the ancestor of the llama and the alpaca

SUB-ORDER RUMINANTIA
Ruminants
This is the most numerous and varied of the artiodactyl groups. All are ruminants (cud chewers) with three or, usually, four chambers in the stomach; their food is brought up from the first chamber and chewed while the animal is resting, before being swallowed a second time for complete digestion. Many have horns or antlers. There are five families:

FAMILY TRAGULIDAE
Chevrotains; 4 species
Chevrotains, also called mouse deer, are very small ruminants without horns. They have three-chambered stomachs, and the males have long, tusk-like canine teeth. They live in the tropical forests of Africa and southern Asia. Example:
Lesser Malay chevrotain *Tragulus javanicus*: it is uniformly brown, unlike other species, which have spotted or striped coats

FAMILY CERVIDAE
Deer; 40 species
Most male deer grow branched antlers—bony outgrowths of the skull covered with velvet (furry skin) during growth. Antler growth stops before the mating season and the velvet is then shed. Antlers are shed after the mating season. The smaller, more delicately built females do not generally have antlers. Examples:
Musk deer *Moschus moschiferus* (20 in. at the shoulder): found in the mountains of central Asia, it has tusk-like canine teeth but no antlers. A musk gland on the abdomen of the male secretes a brownish wax, used in the manufacture of perfume
Red deer *Cervus elaphus*: found in deciduous forests of Europe, Asia and North America. It has large antlers, often 3 ft long. The American race, known as the wapiti or American elk, is sometimes regarded as a separate species *Cervus canadensis*
Pudu *Pudu pudu* (16 in. tall at the shoulder): found in the temperate forests of Bolivia and Chile
Moose *Alces alces* (male more than 6 ft tall at the shoulder): the largest living deer, found in the coniferous forests of Europe and Asia (where it is called the elk) and North America. It is easily recognisable by its characteristic broad, overhanging muzzle
Chinese water deer *Hydropotes inermis* (24 in. tall at the shoulder): found in river valleys in China and Korea and introduced into England and France. It has no antlers but has long, curved tusks

FAMILY BOVIDAE
Cattle and antelopes; 110 species
Bovids have horns with bony cores which grow hard sheaths of horny material. The horns, which are unbranched, are never shed; the sheath is constantly renewed from inside. Most bovids live in grasslands. They vary widely in body form. Examples:
Yak *Bos grunniens* (5 ft 6 in. at shoulder): the wild cattle of the highest plateau of Tibet at altitudes of 15,000–16,500 ft. A smaller, often mottled form is used as a domesticated animal in China and India
Common eland *Taurotragus oryx* (6 ft at the shoulder): a large antelope with straight, spirally twisted horns; it lives on the plains of southern and eastern Africa
Four-horned antelope *Tetracerus quadricornis* (2 ft 6 in. tall at the shoulder): inhabits open woodland in India. The male, with four small horns, is the only living four-horned mammal
European bison *Bison bonasus* (6 ft at the shoulder): formerly widespread in European forests, it is now found only in a few small, protected herds. It has heavy forequarters, a hump on its shoulders and a massive head, but is not as heavily built as the related American species
Grey duiker *Sylvicapra grimmia*: found in open country south of the Sahara. Duikers are small, short-legged African antelopes with a tuft of hair between their short, sharply pointed horns
Defassa waterbuck *Kobus defassa* (4 ft 6 in. tall at the shoulder): a thick-set antelope which lives near water in African grasslands. It has long, coarse hair and large, corrugated horns curved slightly forwards at the tips
Arabian oryx *Oryx leucoryx* (up to 4 ft tall at the shoulder): formerly found in Arabia and Iraq in arid plains and deserts, it has been hunted almost to extinction in the wild. It has long, sharp horns
Hartebeest *Alcelaphus buselaphus* (4 ft 6 in. tall at the shoulder): ranges in large herds on the African plains, and runs swiftly when alarmed. It is an ungainly animal with shoulders higher than the rump. Its horns are lyre-shaped
Royal antelope *Neotragus pygmaeus* (12 in. tall at the shoulder): found in West African forests, it is the smallest ruminant. Its black horns are only about 1 in. long
Blackbuck *Antilope cervicapra* (2 ft 6 in. at the shoulder): the typical antelope of the Indian plains. The adult male is glossy black above, and the females are yellow-fawn; both are white underneath
Saiga antelope *Saiga tatarica* (2 ft 6 in. tall at the shoulder): formerly found throughout the steppes of Europe and Asia and once in danger of extinction, its numbers are now increasing as a result of careful conservation. It is a wary, sheep-like animal with a large swollen muzzle and downward-facing nostrils
Chamois *Rupicapra rupicapra* (2 ft 8 in. tall at the shoulder): found in the Alps, the Pyrénées and most of the other mountain ranges of Europe and Asia Minor; it is a goat-antelope with slender black horns set close together and bending back at the tips to form a hook. It lives in the alpine zone in the summer, descending into the forests in winter
Wild goat *Capra hircus* (3 ft at shoulder): inhabits hilly country in the Aegean islands, Turkey, Iran and Sind; it is the ancestor of the domestic goat. Both sexes have long horns and beards which vary in size according to the race
Musk-ox *Ovibos moschatus* (up to 5 ft at the shoulder): now confined to northern Canada and Greenland. It is more closely related to sheep than to true oxen, and looks like a large, long-coated ram. Its broad, downward-curving horns nearly meet in the middle of the skull
Bighorn sheep *Ovis canadensis* (up to 3 ft 6 in. at the shoulder): found in the mountains of Siberia and western North America, it is the only wild sheep in North America. The male has tightly curved horns with outward-pointing tips and thick bases; the female has very small horns or none at all. It belongs to the same genus as the domestic sheep

FAMILY ANTILOCAPRIDAE
There is one species:
Pronghorn *Antilocapra americana*: lives in North American grasslands. Both sexes have horns consisting of fused hairs sheathing a bony core; the sheath is shed each year

FAMILY GIRAFFIDAE
Giraffes; 2 species
The two or three horns of the giraffe and okapi (absent in the female okapi) are bony growths covered by skin
Giraffe *Giraffa camelopardalis*: lives in small herds on the African savanna, ranging into the arid zone in western Africa and the Sudan where acacia trees grow. A third horn generally develops on the forehead, and East African races often have an extra small pair of horns behind the main pair, making five in all. The giraffe's prehensile tongue can extend about 20 in. to strip leaves from trees
Okapi *Okapia johnstoni* (5 ft tall at the shoulder): found in rain forest in the eastern Congo, the okapi is a primitive member of the giraffe family, first discovered by Europeans in about 1900. It is like the giraffe in structure, but has a shorter neck and shorter legs

INDEX

Addendum

PHYLUM GNATHOSTOMULIDA

Gnathostomulids; about 50 species.

These are minute, transparent, worm-like animals, never more than 0·04 in. long. The head bears complex jaws and long cilia; the body is covered with short cilia by which they move. They are hermaphrodite with cross fertilization, and the eggs hatch into larvae which resemble the adults. They live in marine muddy sands. They are perhaps related to the free-living flatworms, and should be placed after the phylum Platyhelminthes. Example:

***Gnathostomula jenneri*:** from the littoral of the eastern United States.

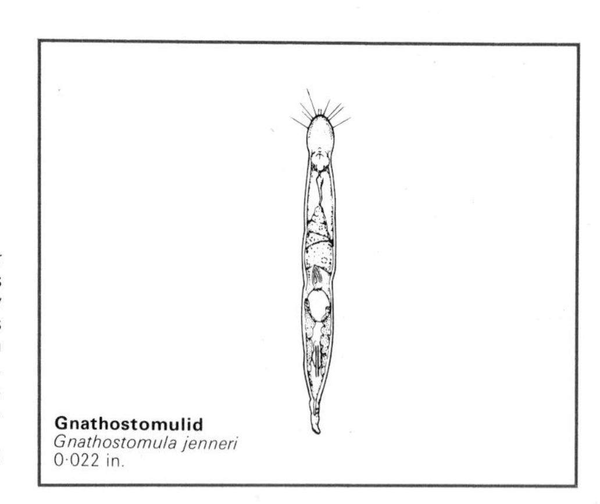

Gnathostomulid
Gnathostomula jenneri
0·022 in.

REFERENCES

The following list contains brief references to works which will help the reader to pursue the classification in more detail, or to study the principles involved. Some works are entered which are concerned with fossil material, so that living animals may be seen in a wider context. In the general list some have been included which are voluminous and costly, but they are to be found in any good zoological library. Others are easily available but contain useful statements of detail. These works should be consulted for those groups which have no special entry. Special entries are given for those large groups on which it is felt likely that readers may want further information. The list has been confined to works in English where possible, but a few in foreign languages have had to be included where no suitable one in English exists. It makes no reference to works which are concerned with the fauna of any particular geographic area except where these contain general considerations of classification of any particular group.

Blackwelder, R. E. *Classification of the animal kingdom.* Carbondale, Ill. 1963.

Clark, R. B. & Panchen, A. L. *Synopsis of animal classification.* London 1971.

Grassé, P. P. *editor. Traité de zoologie.* 17 vols, Paris 1949– . (In progress.)

Hyman, L. H. *The invertebrates.* 6 vols, New York 1940– . (In progress.)

Mayr, E. *Animal species and evolution.* Cambridge, Mass. 1963.

Moore, R. C. & Teichert, C. *editors. Treatise on invertebrate paleontology.* New York & Lawrence, Kan. 1953–. (In progress.)

Piveteau, J. *editor. Traité de paléontologie.* 7 vols, Paris 1952–69.

Rothschild, *Lord. A classification of living animals.* London 1965. Second edition.

Simpson, G. G. The principles of classification and a classification of mammals. *Bull. Amer. Mus. nat. Hist.*, Vol. **85**, 1945.

Simpson, G. G. *Principles of animal taxonomy.* New York 1961.

Insecta—Brues, C. T., Melander, A. L. & Carpenter, F. M. Classification of insects. *Bull. Mus. comp. Zool. Harvard*, Vol. **73**, 1954. Second edition.

Insecta—Imms, A. D. *A general textbook of entomology.* London 1957. 9th edition, revised by O. W. Richards & R. C. Davies.

Insecta etc.—Rodendorf, B. B. *Myriapoda, Insecta and Arachnida.* Vol. **9** in *Palaeontology and geology of the U.S.S.R.* Moscow 1962. In Russian.

Teleostei—Greenwood, P. H. *et al.* Phyletic studies of teleostean fishes, with a provisional classification of living forms. *Bull. Amer. Mus. nat. Hist.*, Vol. **131**, pp. 339–456, 1966.

Aves—Peters, J. L. *et al. Check list of birds of the World.* 13 vols, Cambridge, Mass. 1931– . Vols **1-7**, **9**, **10**, **12-15**. All published to date.

Aves—Thomson, *Sir* A. Landsborough *editor. A new dictionary of birds.* London 1964.

Mammalia—Anderson, S. & Jones, L. K. *Recent mammals of the World; a synopsis of families.* New York 1967.

Mammalia—Simpson, G. G. The principles of classification and a classification of mammals. *Bull. Amer. Mus. nat. Hist.*, Vol. **85**, 1945.

Mammalia—Walker, E. P. *et al. Mammals of the World.* 3 vols, Baltimore 1964–68. Second edition of Vols **1-2**.

ACKNOWLEDGEMENTS

The information and illustrations in *Classification of the Animal Kingdom – an illustrated guide* first appeared in *The Living World of Animals*, published by the Reader's Digest Association Limited.

We gratefully acknowledge the contributions of John F. Oates, B.Sc., who took responsibility in compiling the classification and who played a major part in planning and editing *The Living World of Animals*; and of Peter Jewell, M.A., Ph.D., B.Sc., who was a leading contributor to that book, and who suggested publishing the classification section as a separate book for the use of students.

Our thanks are also due to the following, all of whom provided information that assisted in the compilation of the classification section of *The Living World of Animals*:
Michael Boorer, B.Sc., Dip.Ed., Education Officer, Zoological Society of London.
A. E. Brafield, Ph.D., B.Sc., Lecturer in Zoology, Queen Elizabeth College, University of London.
Gordon B. Corbet, Ph.D., Curator of Mammals, British Museum (Natural History).
Daniel Freeman, Department of Zoology, British Museum (Natural History).
Alice Grandison, B.Sc., Curator of Reptiles and Amphibians, British Museum (Natural History).
P. H. Greenwood, Ph.D., Curator of Freshwater Fish, British Museum (Natural History).
Colin Groves, Ph.D., University Demonstrator in Physical Anthropology, Cambridge University.
Garth Underwood, D.Sc., Principal Lecturer in Zoology, City of London Polytechnic.
Mary Whitear, D.Sc., Ph.D., Reader in Zoology, University College, London.

ISBN 0 340 16445 X

First published in *The Living World of Animals* 1970
This edition 1972
Reprinted 1973, 1978, 1979

Printed and bound in Great Britain for Hodder and Stoughton Educational, a division of Hodder and Stoughton Ltd, Mill Road, Dunton Green, Sevenoaks, Kent, by Hazell Watson and Viney Ltd, Aylesbury, Bucks